Futures Trading in Livestock
Origins and Concepts

HENRY H. BAKKEN
Economist, Educator, Publisher

been deeply involved in
2, when he began working
essor and later professor
omics at the University

nition as an authority in
akken then served as
tural advisor to several
encies of the federal
ton, D.C., Rome, Tokyo
assies in London and

t and lecturer, he has
y of Puerto Rico, the
ities of Chile and the
culture. Professor
f the Organization
Team on Agri-
uerto Rico and
economic
sources.
several

Futures Trading in Livestock-
Origins and Concepts

**CHICAGO
MERCANTILE
EXCHANGE**
1919-1969

50th ANNIVERSARY

[i]

This volume was edited
by
Henry H. Bakken
University of Wisconsin

FUTURES TRADING IN LIVESTOCK
Origins and Concepts

Papers and Comments by:

Ronald J. Frost — *(Foreword)*
Holbrook Working
Everette B. Harris
Henry H. Bakken 2
Gene A. Futrell 2
M. Brice Kirtley 2
Rollo L. Ehrich
Allen B. Paul
Stanley Lammers
Glenn Andersen
Roger W. Gray
Robert E. Schneidau
Walter W. Minger
A. R. Parsons
Roy V. Edwards
Kenneth Monfort
Lee Schuster
Don Paarlberg
Thomas A. Hieronymus

First Edition
Mimir Publishers Inc.,
Madison, Wisconsin
1970

Published by Mimir Publishers Inc.
Madison, Wisconsin

Printed in the U.S.A. by
Worzalla Publishing Company
Stevens Point, Wisconsin

[iv]

FOREWORD

"Where there is much desire to learn, there of necessity will be much arguing, much writing, many opinions; for opinion in good men is but knowledge in the making."

—John Milton

Encouraged by its mushrooming success in frozen pork belly futures, the Chicago Mercantile Exchange studied the feasibility of establishing contract specifications for other livestock futures in the early 1960s.

The fact that many knowledgeable people dismissed the idea as doomed to fail did not deter the Exchange from continuing its research. It had long been axiomatic that a commodity had to be stored to be successfully traded on the futures market. Success in a livestock futures contract would remove storability as a necessary prerequisite, however, and would open a vast new field of activity for commodity exchanges.

The fact that leading authorities from academia, the meat industry, and the futures industry were willing to discuss the ramifications for such a futures contract led to the Exchange-sponsored seminars of November 16, 1967, November 30, 1966 and November 29, 1965.

The papers presented in this book were among those offered. To scholars and others interested in the development of futures trading in meat and livestock, this book is intended to be more than just a record of the first successful excursion by a commodity futures exchange into contracts calling for delivery of live animals.

There are a growing number of books available that explain how to hedge, how to speculate, how to use charts, and other trading information about commodity futures. This book is not intended as a trading guide, but rather to provide students of the markets with the evolution of not only a new contract, but a new concept: practical as well as theoretical views; general observations and specific details.

The papers included here reveal some of the obstacles that had to be overcome, and present an indication of the rewards.

While there is much agreement, there is also dissent. The lively discussions of these authorities provides a wealth of ideas that merit the attention of such students.

[v]

The Chicago Mercantile Exchange provided the forum, but the credit for the papers belongs to the individuals. Although the Chicago Mercantile Exchange was responsible for the meetings, it cannot claim origination for the panelists' ideas; nor does it necessarily agree with all the thoughts presented. Many of the questions posed at the seminars have been resolved; others remain unanswered, although it is a fact that livestock futures have matured into a successful marketing aid.

The papers are presented according to general topic headings and not in chronological order. Two papers; those of Pres. Harris and Dr. Working were not presented at the study conferences.

Special thanks are due to Professor Bakken, University of Wisconsin, for organizing and editing the many papers presented at the conferences, and for his own contributions.

Deep appreciation is also expressed to the participants in the different meetings for sharing their knowledge and experience with students of the market.

Their comments gave Exchange officials the confidence to carry out decisions through a better understanding of the markets, adding exciting new dimensions to livestock marketing.

June 30, 1970   Ronald J. Frost

CONTENTS

Part IV

Experience in the Practical Use of Futures Contracts in the Marketing of Livestock

Part V

Some General Observations Relevant to Trading in Futures

The Board of Governors and Officers, Chicago Mercantile Exchange 1969

The Chicago Mercantile Exchange, 110 N. Franklin St.

Appendixes

Part I

History and Development

Economic Functions of Futures Markets

by
Holbrook Working
Stanford University

I.

There is drama in the story of the Chicago Mercantile Exchange; and reason why the highlights of the story should be noted at the beginning of what may seem a prosaic set of inquiries into economic questions. The dramatic aspects of the story are directly related to major economic issues concerning the functions of commodity exchanges, their usefulness to the society, and the framing of public policy toward them.[1]

The Chicago Mercantile Exchange began in 1898, under the name of the Butter and Egg Board. Like all earlier exchanges in the long history of commerce, it was founded to facilitate strictly cash merchandising transactions. It prospered for a time, although modestly; commerce in butter and eggs was not big business even at Chicago.

---

[1] In telling the story from this standpoint, some aspects are omitted which are covered by Mr. Harris in his paper on the history of the Exchange, and some features are emphasized.

[3]

But presently its merchandising business fell into a severe, sustained decline. Search for some additional line of business, appropriate to its facilities and to the experience and skills of its members, turned thoughts to the possibility of developing futures trading in butter and eggs. Such trading had been a major part of the business of the neighboring Chicago Board of Trade since long before the Butter and Egg Board was formed. Might it be that futures markets could be established in butter and in eggs, despite general opinion that they were not the sort of commodity in which futures trading could succeed? Encouraged by the fact that there already existed a considerable amount of merchandising trade in eggs for forward delivery,[2] the exchange committed itself to the experiment, which seemed to call for a change in name of the exchange. The experiment was only modestly successful at first, but within five years had so expanded the business of the exchange that new and enlarged quarters were needed.

The new prosperity proved shortlived. Merchandising trade in butter and in eggs tended more and more to bypass the exchange, and presently futures trading in those commodities also fell into a decline, particularly that in butter. Impelled once more to seek new lines of business to replace that which it was losing, the exchange turned its thought to other commodities, considering the possibilities for either bringing existing merchandising trade in those commodities onto the exchange, or for establishing futures trading in them. There was slim possibility of success with any commodity that was already being traded on a United States exchange. Might it be possible to develop futures trading in some commodity for which no futures market yet existed?

A long series of efforts in that direction, extending over some thirty years and including commodities ranging from apples to turkeys, and even scrap iron, produced only two successes: a barely marginal success with futures trading in Idaho potatoes (why in Idaho potatoes, and not in the kind of potatoes grown closer to Chicago and in greater quantity?), and a substantial success with onions (why onions, but not with apples?).

---

[2] Irwin, H. S., The Evolution of Futures Trading, Mimir Publishers Inc., Madison Wis., 1954.

Then in 1958 futures trading in onions, which had become a major part of the business of the exchange, was prohibited by an act of Congress.[3]

At this point the outlook for the Chicago Mercantile Exchange might have been judged hopeless. It had lost virtually all merchandising trade, such as had been its sole support while it went under the name of the Butter and Egg Board. Futures trading in butter had long since died out. Futures trading in eggs was threatened with decline, owing to reduction in the seasonality of egg production and consequent diminution in the storage of eggs. Its futures market in potatoes showed no prospect of developing much business — most traders in potatoes preferred to use the larger and more fluid New York market. And that feeble potato futures market was the sole survivor from thirty years of efforts to develop new business.

But the Exchange refused to accept the verdict that it must be a victim of technological unemployment at the age of 40 (counting from the time when it was born as a commodity futures exchange). And ten years later its president could point to statistics showing that in August 1969 the Chicago Mercantile Exchange had done more business than any other exchange in the United States.[4] That meant, in fact, more business than any other exchange in the world.

II

Anyone who reflects on the events summarized above must find a number of questions coming to mind. Foremost among these may be the questions: Why did an exchange that was organized solely to facilitate direct merchandising trade, abandon that function and concentrate its efforts on promoting futures trading? What are the consequences for society of such a change?

These might seem questions of small significance if they arose only in one instance, in the evolution of a single commodity exchange. But what has happened on the Chicago Mercantile Exchange in this respect has been happening, sometimes

[3] Public Law 85-839.
[4] See Table 3, p. 53 below.

less quickly and less conspicuously, to commodity exchanges throughout the commercially developed world — though not always with the emergence of futures trading to take the place of vanished merchandising trade.

1.

The first question posed above, though it tends to be raised initially in that form, misstates the facts. The Chicago Mercantile Exchange, and other exchanges with a like experience, did not abandon their function of promoting merchandising trade; merchandising trade abandoned them. The kind of trade that in former days had gravitated toward the organized exchanges tended more and more, with the passing years, to bypass them. The merchandising trade continued, of course, perhaps carried on principally by members of the exchange, but not in organized trading sessions on the exchange floor.

Such bypassing of the organized exchange occurred with exceptional rapidity on the Chicago Mercantile Exchange because of special circumstances affecting trade in butter and in eggs; but it was occurring everywhere else throughout the commercially developed world, under the influence of a common set of forces. Four major developments, it seems to me, contributed to the result.

The most obvious of these influences was communications technology. Commodity exchanges got their start because merchants needed to assemble in one place in order to bargain over the price, under conditions that would allow each participant in a transaction to feel confident that he had struck about as good a bargain as was possible at that time. Rapid communication among a considerable number of potential buyers and sellers, needing to know what others were willing to sell for, or what price they would pay, was possible only if they got together in person. The telephone and the teletype changed that, reducing the need for merchants to gather in one place in order to bargain satisfactorily.

A second influence was the growing concentration of trade into the hands of a few large firms, centrally located in the merchandising chain. When that concentration had gone far enough, any one of those firms needed only to make a few telephone calls to get all of the information that, formerly, would have been obtained through attendance on the exchange floor.

Another development, furthered in part by growth in the size of individual merchandising and processing firms, was an increasing tendency to enter into transactions involving delivery of the commodity at some more or less distant date, perhaps several months ahead. This produced a fragmentation of the market, from the standpoint of price, inasmuch as prices would differ according to the date specified for delivery. Such forward merchandising transactions very early became dominant in the wheat import trade of Britain, and the consequences may be observed in the price quotations recorded in *Broomhall's Corn Trade News*. Prices were quoted separately on "parcels" and on cargoes, and might differ accordingly; and they tended to differ according to the specified time of shipment or of expected arrival of the parcel or cargo. A degree of sophistication was required to interpret such a set of price quotations. When a somewhat similar situation developed on domestic markets in the United States, it may have contributed somewhat to the decline in use of the exchanges as places in which to execute merchandising transactions, inasmuch as one of the purposes of such an exchange was to provide the public with price information. Information that was hard to interpret might seem not worth providing.

Finally, if a futures market was established on an exchange, its existence tended to promote the diversion of merchandising trade from the exchange. Futures price quotations, instantly available, give a merchant or processor much of the information that he would otherwise seek through going to the exchange floor. Knowing the current futures price, buyer and seller can often come to agreement in the office, with both present, or talking over the telephone, whereas, otherwise they would want the wider bargaining opportunity offered by an exchange floor. And when most merchandising trade has bypassed an exchange, the exchange floor no longer offers wide bargaining opportunity.

Let me return for a moment to the matter of historical changes in the prevalence of forward merchandising trade. Charles H.

Taylor, historian of the Chicago Board of Trade, held that trade in futures began "in a perfectly natural way", growing out of the use of "to arrive" contracts, namely, sales made by country merchants on terms such as ". . . 'to arrive in 5 days' or 'to arrive in 10 days' . . .".[5] It may seem strange that any great amount of speculation should have arisen in contracts that ran for no more than 5 or 10 days, and thus, have led to the establishment of organized futures trading on the exchange; but inasmuch as Taylor's membership on the Board of Trade dated from 1868,[6] his statement was unquestioningly accepted. It carried with it the implication that "to arrive" contracts were the only forward contracts in common use in the grain trade prior to the establishment of organized futures trading.

Taylor's opinion was challenged, nearly forty years later, by H. S. Irwin, on the basis of a study of evidence from primary sources,[7] but without pointing out, as he might have, that Taylor's opinion was inconsistent with his own account of the facts. At numerous points in his chronological account Taylor mentions speculative activity, and usually specifies its nature. Concerning speculation in 1850 he notes that ". . . on the 18th of October some enthusiastic 'bear' sold 30,000 bushels of corn for delivery in June 1851 . . . the first recorded sale of any grain for delivery so far in the future."[8] His account for 1851 remarks on "a noticeable increase in the quantity of corn sold for future delivery, especially during the months of March and April, when several sales for June delivery were made. (Note that these were not what we should now call futures transactions; 14 years were yet to elapse before the Chicago Board of Trade adopted a standardized futures contract and thus initiated organized futures trading in the United States).

Taylor's next comments on speculation apply to 1854. "Sales for future delivery were increasingly frequent in 1854," he

---

[5] Taylor, C. H., History of the Board of Trade of the City of Chicago, Robert O. Law Co., Chicago (1917), Vol. I, p. 193.
[6] Ibid., Vol. III, p. 317.
[7] Irwin, H. S., Evolution of Futures Trading, Mimir Publishers, Inc., Madison, Wisconsin (1954), pp. 69-83.
[8] Taylor, History, Vol I, p. 164.

writes, ". . . not confined to the Chicago grain market. New Orleans papers of the 13th of January reported a contract for 150,000 bushels of corn deliverable in the following March and April".[9] In the next paragraph he quotes the St. Louis *Evening News* as having reported: "Wheat contracts, flour contracts, and purchases of corn, weeks and months since, during the inflation, are beginning to mature . . ." And following that he writes: "The 'Journal' (Chicago) of April 21st says that "the purchaser of 100,000 bushels of corn . . . contracted to be delivered on board in July has realized a cool $3,000.00 by a re-sale . . ."[10] At no place that I have found does Taylor mention any noteworthy amount of speculation in "to arrive" contracts.

How then can we account for Taylor's opinion that futures trading had its origin in speculative use of "to arrive" contracts? The most plausible explanation that has come to my mind begins with the supposition that the establishment of organized futures trading on the Chicago Board of Trade in 1865, providing assurance that contracts would be fulfilled through either delivery of the kind and quality of commodity specified or an equivalent financial settlement, led both speculators and handlers of the commodity to turn quickly to the use of those contracts in place of the kinds of forward contract previously in use. Thus it came about that Taylor, having entered the grain trade three years later, observed only two sorts of forward contract in common use, namely the futures contracts of the exchange, and "to arrive" contracts. It would have been natural for him to assume that futures trading, as he knew it from direct observation, had arisen through the emergence of speculation in "to arrive" contracts. When, years later, he began a study of the history of trade at Chicago, he recorded what he learned and set down, along with this newly acquired information, his previously formed opinion about the origin of futures trading, failing to recognize its inconsistency with the history of trade that he was presenting. Such failures to fully adjust one's thinking to newly acquired information are hard to avoid, as I know from my own experience.

---

[9] Ibid, p. 192.
[10] Ibid, p. 193.

FUTURES TRADING IN LIVESTOCK

Whether that be the true explanation of Taylor's inconsistency or not, it is clear that forward merchandising contracts were in fairly wide use in the United States around the middle of the last century, and there is at least strong reason to believe that the emergence of organized futures trading led to a sharp decline in the use of forward contracts other than those administered by the exchange. More recently, if my impression is correct, there has been a rather widespread resurgence of forward merchandising trade, aided in some instances by the existence of a futures market. In the case that I know best, large baking firms, progressively displacing small bakeries during several decades following World War I, have tended commonly to place flour orders months in advance instead of buying from hand to mouth, as is usual with small bakeries. Flour millers were led, in consequence, to do more forward buying of wheat than formerly, (most flour millers lacked the storage capacity to carry wheat stocks equivalent in amount to their unfilled flour orders at times when baking firms had bought heavily forward). And millers were the more willing to accept large forward orders for flour because they could immediately buy an equivalent amount of wheat futures, to be held pending the making of merchandising contracts for the wheat to be milled. On September 30 of almost any recent year, mills reporting to the Millers National Federation have held unfilled flour orders equivalent to somewhat over three months' production. On that date in 1967, a year in which the figures were at near average levels for recent years, the reporting mills showed aggregate positions as follows, in million bushels:

Unfilled flour orders, as wheat	98
Wheat futures sold	13
Total	111
Wheat in store or brought forward	89
Flour stocks, as wheat	9
Wheat futures bought	16
Total	114

Though the reporting mills, in the aggregate, owned wheat and held flour stocks in an amount almost exactly equivalent to their unfilled flour orders, many individual mills had either an excess of unfilled orders, or an excess of wheat owned plus flour stocks, and had accordingly taken a long or a short position in the futures market.

2.

The disappearance of merchandising trade from the exchanges had serious consequences. By the early 1920's people in the dairy industry were complaining that butter prices in transactions on the Chicago Mercantile Exchange were based on such a tiny fraction of the merchandising trade in butter as to be unreliable. The recorded transactions, on which prices were made public, were said to be always for small quantities. They were suspected of being "rigged", to give butter producers a false impression of the price that they ought to be able to obtain for their product. The market news service of the U.S. Department of Agriculture was initiated at that time in an effort to give producers more reliable information on prevailing prices of butter and of numerous other commodities.

Another consequence of bypassing of the exchanges became particularly conspicuous in the hog trade in the 1920's. There, bypassing of the exchanges took the form of a rise in country buying of hogs by the packers. Country buying brought substantial economies to the hog trade, but it also meant that the producer sold with little opportunity to get competitive bids. Sometimes he had to accept whatever price a single buyer would offer. And the central market became a less reliable guide to what price he ought to be able to obtain — or at any rate it became a less trusted guide.[11]

---

[11] This and the preceding paragraph have been written primarily from memory of verbal discussions at the time. Records exist in which the developments that are here so briefly summarized can be studied in some detail, but I cannot conveniently supply references.

[11]

When I made a study of onion prices over the period from 1930 onward,[12] the only good "cash" price quotations available seemed to be those compiled officially by the Market News Service. Its central market quotations (at Chicago) covered too few transactions per week to afford a good price series for onions of any one kind and quality. The best available price series for a more or less central location in the United States appeared to be the Market News Service compilation of daily prices at country points in Michigan. And of course, those were prices at points where the degree of competition among buyers was open to some question.

3.

The establishment of a futures market on an exchange that has lost most or all of its merchandising trade serves to provide central-market prices arrived at in highly competitive bargaining, like the prices formerly available on merchandising transactions executed on the exchange. Moreover, the futures prices quoted for several different delivery months are potentially more informative than prices covering only spot transactions, involving immediate delivery.

But only a part of the potential public usefulness of futures-market price quotations has been realized, owing partly to inadequate knowledge, and partly to a grave misconception.

Inadequate knowledge has prevented many people, interested primarily in the spot price, from recognizing that the futures prices, at most times, give a reliable basis for estimating an equivalent spot price. The knowledge needed to permit such estimation is not difficult to acquire. And a person interested in the spot price is usually interested also in an estimate of what the price will be in the future. Futures prices give him directly the consensus of market opinion on that point.

More serious than inadequate knowledge has been the widespread belief that futures prices are not prices on the actual commodity. That belief manifested itself early, in the form of

12 Working, Holbrook, "Price Effects of Futures Trading", *Food Research Institute Studies*, Vol. I, pp. 3-31. February 1960.

attacks on trading in "phantom wheat". Members of the trade — trade in each of a variety of different commodities — have used the expression "transactions in the actual commodity" to designate transactions other than in futures, thereby promoting the false idea that futures trading is not trading in the actual commodity.

If the Westinghouse Electric Company sells half-a-dozen huge generators to, say, the Ohio Edison Company a year or more before the generators are built, no one would call that transaction a sale of phantom generators. If I buy a Volkswagen for delivery in Paris two months hence, and buy it from a firm that will itself have to go out and buy a VW in order to make delivery to me (the sort of transaction that many people make before starting on a trip to Europe) no one would think of saying that I had bought a phantom Volkswagen. Why, then, think of futures contracts for wheat or for cattle as anything but contracts for the actual commodity? They *are* contracts for the actual commodity, just as truly as are the contracts for generators and a Volkswagen in the foregoing examples.

III

The most dramatic feature in the history of the Chicago Mercantile Exchange was the abrupt turn in its fortunes at about 1960. During three prior decades, it had made a long series of attempts, one after the other, to add new commodities to the short list of those for which it maintained futures markets. All but two of those attempts failed. Meanwhile its futures market in onions was struck down by federal legislation. Between 1960 and 1966, the exchange made three more attempts to establish a new futures market; and every one of the three was a conspicuous success.

Among the reasons for this remarkable change in the fortunes of the exchange was the emergence and acceptance of a new idea to guide the choice of a commodity in which to introduce futures trading: the idea that a futures market could succeed only to the degree that it could attract business from handlers of the commodity.

That idea, I believe, was first advanced explicitly and publicly in 1953.[13] It tended at first to seem a dubious theory. But almost immediately it received striking confirmation. Primary credit for this new idea should go to the man who started collection of the data that were to produce the first, and still the strongest, evidence that something was wrong with the traditional concept of a futures market. Dr. J. W. T. Duvel, first Chief of the Grain Futures Administration (later, the Commodity Exchange Authority) had been trained in the natural sciences, and believed in the need for research based on relevant quantitative information. He had learned much about futures markets while directing grain standardization investigations for the U.S. Department of Agriculture, serving during World War I with the U.S. Grain Corporation, and later working briefly as a grain merchant himself. He believed it necessary to have statistics on open futures contracts, shown separately so far as possible, for speculators and for hedgers. Over strenuous objection from the grain exchanges, he instituted the collection of such statistics.

As these statistics accumulated during the later 1920's, they began to show an unexpected characteristic, inconsistent with the view, then accepted everywhere, that the existence and amount of futures trading depended entirely on the desire of people to speculate. Total open contracts on each futures market showed a strange tendency to vary in fairly close correspondence with the amount of "hedging" contracts outstanding.[14]

---

[13] Working, Holbrook, "Futures Trading and Hedging", *American Economic Review,* June 1953, 43, pp. 318-20.

[14] I put the term "hedging" in quotation marks throughout the remainder of this essay, as a continuing reminder that the word means different things to different people and in different contexts. Here it means "hedging" as originally defined by the Commodity Exchange Act. That definition was broadened substantially in 1956 by Congressional amendment of the Act. Many economists have defined "hedging" much more narrowly than did the original Commodity Exchange Act, though they would also have accepted as valid the definition in the Act, unaware that it was in fact a much broader definition than their own. (The narrowness of their definition brought a disaster to the Chicago Mercantile Exchange, as we shall see later). At the other extreme, many businessmen would class as "hedging" *any* use of commodity futures by a business firm in the normal conduct of a business involved in producing, storing, merchandising, or processing either that commodity, or some other more or less closely related commodity.

This strange characteristic of the statistics gradually became well known to members of commodity exchanges and to economists interested in futures markets. It was emphasized, with ample supporting evidence, in a widely circulated publication by Duvel and Hoffman.[15] But for a quarter-century after the fact became visible in the statistics, no one seemed to recognize that it required a change in thinking about futures markets. As Conant has written concerning science in general, ". . . a theory is only overthrown by a better theory, never merely by contradictory facts."[16] In this case the contradictory facts seemed to point to a theory that the amount of total business done on a futures market depends on the amount of business that is attracted from handlers of the commodity, and no one could see any logical reason for believing that to be true.

Then in 1942 H.S. Irwin, an economist brought to the Commodity Exchange Authority by Duvel, began inquiring into the origin of futures trading on the Chicago Mercantile Exchange. He was spurred by a desire to take advantage, before it was too late, of drawing on the memories of older members of the Exchange.[17] His final conclusions, however, were based more on evidence from contemporary documents than on fallible personal memories.

His findings, briefly summarized and with attention only to eggs, were that egg dealers, accumulating stocks during the months of heavy production, very early began seeking purchasers who would buy for delivery months later, when production was light. As early as 1895 much of the buying on such forward contracts was by speculators. The amount of such trade increased substantially during the next two decades.[18] Finally, in 1919, a

---

[15] Hoffman, G.W. and J.W.T. Duvel, *Grain Prices and the Futures Market.* U.S. Dept. of Agr., Tech. Bul. No. 747 (1941).

[16] Conant, James B., *On Understanding Science,* Yale University Press, 1947, p. 36. Anyone who thinks it strange that people took so long to see the significance of the evidence in the open-contract statistics will find it interesting to read two or three pages that precede and follow the brief observation of Conant's that is quoted above.

[17] Irwin, H.S., *Evolution of Futures Trading,* Mimir Publishers, Inc., Madison, Wisconsin (1954), p. ix.

[18] Ibid, pp. 28, 29.

group of members of the Butter and Egg Board initiated plans for a new exchange to provide needed supervision and control of the hitherto unorganized futures trading in butter and eggs. But on second thought it was decided that the new function should be assumed by the existing exchange, under the new name, Chicago Mercantile Exchange.[19] Thus, Irwin concluded, futures trading in eggs had arisen in response to a desire of handlers of the commodity to "hedge". And so it was also with butter.

Though Irwin's conclusions concerning the origin of futures trading in butter and eggs did not reach print until 1954, he put them initially into a paper that he sent me in 1946. At first I was unconvinced. But on reflection, I recognized that Irwin's conclusion about the origin of futures trading on the Chicago Mercantile Exchange was in accord with facts that Hoos and I had noted in our study of the origin and development of futures trading in wheat at Liverpool. [20] And they pointed in the same direction as did the statistics on open contracts, namely, to the conclusion that futures trading is directly dependent on use of the futures market by handlers of the commodity. Moreover, acceptance of that conclusion would allow accounting, at least roughly, for the great differences in amounts of futures trading in different commodities, for which no other reasonable explanation had been found. I was finally convinced that the theory that futures trading has its basis in use of the futures market by handlers of the commodity must be accepted as true, even though we could not see why that should be so.[21]

---

[19] Ibid, pp. 39, 40.

[20] Working, Holbrook and S. Hoos, "Wheat Futures Prices and Trading at Liverpool Since 1886", *Wheat Studies of the Food Research Institute,* XV, pp. 142 ff. (November 1938).

[21] The question, Why? has continued to intrigue me. A first step toward an answer was made through discovering the functional relations between speculation and "hedging", as measured by open contracts. The equation for "short" speculation necessarily differs from that for "long" speculation; and each equation shows the effect of "long hedging" to be different from that of "short hedging" ("Speculation on Hedging Markets", *Food Research Institute Studies,* Vol. I, pp. 194-97 (May 1960).

A second step was made through finding evidence that "scalpers" (one class of speculators) derive much of their income directly from "hedgers", as a return for the scalpers' service in contributing to the fluidity of the market; and that scalpers tend continually to lose money to "news traders" ("Tests of a Theory Concerning Floor Trading on Commodity Exchanges", *Food Research Institute*

If it had been in my power to arrange a scientific experiment to test that theory, I would have sought out an exchange that could easily lose its "hedging" business to another exchange. Then I would have arranged for that exchange to alter its futures contract in a way that was objectionable to hedgers, but that did not change the attractiveness of the contract to speculaors. By remarkable coincidence, just such an exchange did almost exactly that in 1953, simultaneously with the appearance in print of a paper in which I committed myself to the theory.

The results of the experiment being initiated by that exchange would surely deserve recording, hence I sought information on the reasoning that had led the exchange to decide on the alteration of its futures contract. The information was generously provided in the form of a file of letters submitted by exchange members to the committee studying the proposal. They showed that most "hedgers" on the exchange strenuously opposed the alteration in contract terms, whereas others favored it on the ground that it could be expected to attract increased speculative trading.

It was apparent therefore that, by the standards of scientific experimentation, the design of this experiment was faulty; the alteration in contract terms should have been such as to leave unchanged the attractiveness of the contract to speculators. But that did not matter. The exchange promptly lost most of its futures business, both "hedging" and speculative.[22]

Besides the evidence summarized above, officers and members of the Chicago Mercantile Exchange had the evidence from their own experience while they had been seeking to establish

Studies, VII, Supplement [1967], pp. 5-48). Thus we have two classes of speculators whose incomes depend directly and immediately on "hedging" transactions. Why "price-level traders" also tend to enter or to leave a futures market in at least fairly prompt response to increase or decrease in the amount of "hedging", as they appear to do, remains a question at whose answer we can still only guess, with little hard evidence by which to confirm or to refute anybody's guess. My guess is that at least two lines of influence operate to produce this result. Some scalpers and most "news traders" tend to engage in some price-level trading also, and to do so where and when they find the other, more reliably remunerative, kind of trading profitable. Secondly, I surmise, those speculators who seek profit chiefly or wholly from price-level trading tend to do so in markets and at times when they see evidence that other speculators are making money.

[22] Working, Holbrook, "Whose Markets — Evidence on Some Aspects of Futures Trading", *Journal of Marketing,* XIX, pp. 7-9 (July, 1954).

futures trading in commodities that they thought would attract speculative interest. In their later efforts, they sought commodities whose handlers — producers, merchants, warehousers, or processors — would want to make substantial use of a futures market. Their own experience showed that if they could attract enough "hedging" to a new futures market, they could attract to it also the speculation that would allow the market to succeed.

IV

Though any futures market succeeds only to the degree that it can attract "hedging" use, that is not the only requisite to success. I would list four conditions as necessary for a futures market to survive and prosper. They are:

1. The contract terms and commission charges must be such as to attract appreciable use of the futures contract for merchandising purposes.
2. There must exist a possibility of attracting enough speculation to provide at least a reasonably fluid market.
3. Handlers of the commodity must have reason to make substantial use of the futures contracts as temporary substitutes for merchandising contracts that they will make later.[23]
4. There must exist adequate public recognition of the economic usefulness of the futures market.

Each of these four basic requisites carries with it certain subsidiary requirements, but they can differ according to circumstances. Let us consider these basic requirements further.

1.

Suitability of the futures contract for merchandising use (so far as is consistent with its need to be a highly standardized contract in order to attract speculative use) has been most clearly revealed as necessary through a recent study by Powers and Johnson.[24] The need to meet that condition has been overlooked in

---

[23] This is "hedging", according to a definition that I once proposed ("Hedging Reconsidered", *Journal of Farm Economics*, Nov. 1953, 35, p. 560); but that definition has not won enough acceptance to allow using the term here with confidence that it will carry the intended meaning.

[24] Powers, M.J. and A.C. Johnson, Jr., *The Frozen Pork Belly Futures Market*, Univ. of Wisc., Dept. of Agricultural Economics, Bulletin No. 51, Feb. 1968.

the past, we may surmise, for much the same reason that air is not ordinarily listed as a requisite to human life. Most futures markets have arisen either spontaneously, through the emergence of speculation in forward contracts that were already being used in merchandising, or as a result of exchange action in establishing specifications for a futures contract, guided by contract terms that were already being much used in merchandising trade. But in the case studied by Powers and Johnson the exchange, lacking guidance from any well established forward merchandising trade in the commodity, adopted contract terms that proved ill suited to merchandising use of the contract.

The case arose from adoption by the Chicago Mercantile Exchange, in 1961, of contract terms for trading in frozen pork bellies. The contract went virtually unused because potential buyers were reluctant to accept delivery under the contract terms. Revision of the contract for deliveries in 1962 brought it only a little added use, and further revision was made for deliveries in 1963. Then followed two more years during which the chief use of the futures contract by handlers of the commodity was for merchandising, as is evidenced by high ratios of deliveries to maximum open interest in contracts for delivery in any given month. Even in 1965, deliveries on the May and the July contracts were 41 and 56 percent, respectively, of the highest total open interest attained by those contracts.[25] Only later did "hedging" use of the contract expand enough to raise open contract totals to levels that were large multiples of the amounts on which delivery was made.

No other study that I know of for what may be called the period of infancy and adolescence of a futures market, has assembled data on deliveries as well as on open contracts, as did Powers and Johnson. But the course followed by open contracts during the earliest years of futures trading in a commodity has been noted in a few instances, and in each such instance that has come to my attention open contracts followed a course roughly similar to that of open contracts in frozen pork bellies, after the perfection of that contract. Irwin points out that contracts in butter and

---

[25] Op. cit., p. 25.

egg futures remained relatively small in total volume into 1924, and then increased by a factor of two or more.[26] I found that open contracts in onion futures, at the time of year when they tend to approximate their maximum, amounted to only about 2 percent of estimated total United States stocks of onions in each of the first two years of futures trading in that commodity following World War II. In the third year they rose to 3.6 percent, in the fourth year, 1949, to 11.7 percent. Thereafter, until futures trading in onions was made illegal, open contracts in onions on October 15 only once failed to reach at least 9.2 percent of estimated total stocks, and in one year, 1955, reached 23.6 percent.[27]

In a mature futures market, merchandising use of the futures contract becomes a small, sometimes negligibly small, fraction of total use of the contract by handlers of the commodity. It remains necessary, however, for the contract terms to be such as favor some merchandising use, if only because much "hedging" use of the contract is conditioned on contract terms such as favor merchandising use. And commission charges must be even lower to attract much "hedging" use of a contract than to attract merchandising use, because the "hedger" must also, subsequently, make a merchandising contract.

Some authorities on futures trading have held that it is not necessary for a futures market to be usable for merchandising — that deliveries on futures contracts might be eliminated entirely. That is probably true, once "hedging" use of the market has become well established. But "hedgers" must know precisely what kind and quality of the commodity, in what location, is covered by the futures contract; and they must be assured that contracts will be fulfilled in accordance with the contract terms, either by delivery or by an equivalent financial settlement.

Experience has amply demonstrated that it is necessary at times to require holders of futures contracts to accept financial settlement, instead of allowing them to insist that delivery be

[26] Irwin, H.S., *Evolution of Futures Trading*, Mimir Publishers Inc., Madison, Wis., p. 46.
[27] Working, Holbrook, "Price Effects of Futures Trading", *Food Research Institute Studies,* 1, p. 10 (February 1960).

made.[28] When that must be done, a heavy responsibility falls on the committee, or other agency, charged with determining what is an "equivalent financial settlement". If deliveries were done away with, that responsibility would have to be assumed in every "delivery" month, instead of only occasionally.

The "delivery problem", which has given rise to the suggestion that deliveries might be dispensed with, appears to have proved serious only on futures markets in the United States. It has its basis in laws and legal precedents that have made it necessary for exchanges in the United States to require that actual delivery be made, when demanded, under all except the most extraordinary circumstances, in order to assure that brokerage firms shall be able to collect from speculators who have lost money. Time and again such speculators have sought to evade payment by claiming that the futures transaction amounted only to a wager on the price, and courts have taken the position that payment could be enforced under the law only on a showing of intent of the seller to deliver on the futures contract, or of the buyer to accept delivery, or of such intentions on the part of both seller and buyer. The requirements in that respect have differed from state to state.[29]

In this situation the courts, including the U.S. Supreme Court, have been led into what seem to me extraordinary exercises in sophistry in order to hold that the requisite intent was present, and thus to render a just decision, despite absence of any real intention by the parties to make or to receive delivery in the amounts involved.[30] But there are limits on the extent to which the courts can be expected to strain common sense in order to do justice in the presence of laws against wagering, hence exchanges in the United States have felt compelled to make a strong showing of presumption that futures contracts will be settled by

---

[28] Conspicuous distortions of the price structure arising from excessive delivery demands occur only when buyers demand delivery in abnormal amounts, but it has been alleged, on what appear to me valid grounds, that lesser distortions have often been produced by sellers, through their insistence on the acceptance of abnormally heavy deliveries.

[29] See Federal Trade Commission, *Report on the Grain Trade*, Vol. V, p. 314 (1920).

[30] Ibid, pp. 272-318.

delivery. Under those conditions it is not possible for an exchange to avoid the occurence of an occasional squeeze.

It is hazardous for an economist to venture an opinion on a legal matter, but it appears to me that if federal legislation were enacted, perhaps in the form of a brief amendment to the Commodity Exchange Act, declaring all futures contracts executed on an organized exchange to be commercial contracts, enforceable under the law, the exchanges themselves might then speedily solve the delivery problem. On the Liverpool wheat market, which might be judged peculiarly susceptible to corners and squeezes owing to limited facilities for holding wheat available for delivery on futures contracts, no detectible corner or squeeze has ever occurred. Queried as to the reason, the Secretary of the Liverpool Corn Trade Association attributed it to the fact that, in England, "There is no rule of the Association that the Seller must deliver the wheat against his Contract. There is no rule of law that he must do so." He then went on to explain procedures for arriving at an equivalent financial settlement when that is necessary.[31]

2.

Need for a futures market to attract speculation arises immediately after any new futures market has begun to attract merchandising use by handlers of the commodity. The new futures contract in frozen pork bellies, for example, was immediately attractive to firms that were accumulating storage stocks of the commodity because it offered opportunity to make forward sales at a low commission rate. As soon as the original, defective, contract was suitably revised, potential buyers, anticipating their needs for pork bellies to process into bacon, also found it advantageous to use the futures contract, for the same reason. But potential buyers do not automatically appear in such a market at the same time that a holder of the commodity wants to make a forward sale. The potential buyers are likely to hold aloof for awhile, awaiting the inducement of price concessions.

---

[31] Working, Holbrook and S. Hoos, "Wheat Futures Prices and Trading at Liverpool Since 1886", *Wheat Studies of the Food Research Institute,* 15, p. 138 (November 1938).

HISTORY AND DEVELOPMENT

At this point, speculators can find opportunity for profit by stepping in, initially as buyers, and later reselling to processors or to some other speculator. Any one speculator may operate merely as a "scalper", buying when a selling offer gives opportunity to purchase at a slight price reduction, in the expectation of reselling soon afterward when a buying order appears in the market; or he may buy in the expectation of holding for some longer interval of time, anticipating more than some small recovery from a dip.

The accompanying table gives some indication of the extent of speculative participation in futures markets, as measured by

Table 1. — Holdings of Open Futures Contracts by Handlers
of the Commodity and by Speculators Respectively,
Selected Commodities and Dates*

Commodity and date	Commodity handlers		Others (speculators)		Percentage held by speculators	
	Long	Short	Long	Short	Long	Short
Cotton[a]						
Sept. 28, 1956	1,378	1,503	497	373	26	20
Corn[b]						
Sept. 29, 1961	41.6	56.8	113.8	98.6	73	63
Jan. 27, 1967	194.6	237.6	172.7	130.0	47	35
Soybeans[b]						
Nov. 30, 1959	58.9	104.8	133.0	88.9	69	46
Wheat[b]						
Aug. 31, 1964	53.8	99.8	120.9	74.4	69	43
Eggs[c]						
July 29, 1960	2,454[d]	5,152[d]	8,043[e]	5,345[e]	76	51
Onions[c]						
Sept. 30, 1955	4,729	5,418	2,359	1,670	33	24
May 31, 1956	778	1,518	1,190	450	60	23
Aug. 31, 1956	2,405	3,749	2,024	680	46	15
Oct. 31, 1956	2,363	3,699	1,942	606	45	14
Dec. 31, 1956	2,397	3,363	1,940	974	45	22

* Data from Commodity Exchange Authority, *Surveys of Open Contracts* (Mimeo.), including producers of the commodity among its handlers.

[a] Thousand bales; New York and New Orleans Exchanges combined.

[b] Million bushels; Chicago Board of Trade; contracts shown as held by handlers of this commodity may include small amounts held by farmers who did not produce the commodity.

[c] Carlots; Chicago Mercantile Exchange.

[d] Including contracts held by persons in wholesale and retail trade, most of whom presumably dealt in eggs.

[e] Including contracts reported for non-clearing commission merchants, not classified by occupation of the contract holder, but assumed to be held almost wholly by "others" on the ground that their long positions totalled nearly three times as much as their short positions, quite unlike any known class of egg handler.

volume of open contracts. The proportion of open contracts held by speculators (persons other than handlers of the commodity) can vary substantially from time to time in any one market, not only in accordance with fluctuations in degree of speculative interest in the commodity, but also (inversely) as handlers of the commodity have increased or decreased reason to use the futures market for "hedging". It would be unwise, therefore, to take these fragmentary data[32] as evidence that any one of the commodity markets represented in the table has tended to be more or less strongly speculative than another. It is clear, however, that the proportion of open contracts held by speculators tends to be substantially greater for long contracts than for short contracts. In this table the median percentages held by speculators are 47 percent for long contracts and 24 percent for short contracts.

Without speculation a so-called futures market would in fact be only a forward merchandising market, not a true futures market, even though its contracts were called "futures" contracts, and its price quotations published under the name of "futures" prices. And without a liberal volume of speculation no futures market could pay its way from commission charges as low as those on true futures markets, where they normally amount to less than 1 percent of the price on a transaction (charge to non-members of the exchange, and covering a "round turn", both purchase and sale). Such low commission rates are made possible in part by provisions that tend to minimize the cost of executing any one transaction; standardization of contract terms and assumption by the exchange of responsibility for assuring fulfillment of the contract are among those cost-reducing provisions. But total cost per contract, including the overhead cost to the exchange of assuring fulfillment of all contracts in accordance with their terms, cannot be kept so extraordinarily low unless the volume of transactions is large. And volume of transactions depends much more on speculative trade than on use of the futures contract by handlers of the commodity.

---

[32] Statistics of open contracts, classified according to whether held by handlers of the commodity or by others, have been made available only in connection with special surveys, of which there have been very few, except for the series of surveys on onions, utilized here, and a somewhat similar series for potatoes.

HISTORY AND DEVELOPMENT

It was long believed, by exchange members and economists alike, that speculative trade on a futures market could be expanded independently of the amount of business attracted from handlers of the commodity. This has been proved untrue, as we have seen above. Speculation in frozen pork bellies — to continue with that concrete example — could not have attained large volume, except perhaps briefly in some surge of speculative interest that could not have been long sustained, unless handlers of the commodity had been led to use the futures contract for other purposes in addition to merchandising. Such expanded use of the futures contract by handlers of the commodity was needed to provide the broader base on which increased speculative trade could arise.

When a commodity handler uses futures contracts otherwise than for merchandising, having no intention of making or receiving delivery on the contracts, the futures contracts are serving him only as a temporary substitute for a merchandising contract that will be made later. He does not directly cut his cost, as is the case with merchandising use of a futures contract, but incurs an added cost. He does so, of course, either in the belief that he will thus be enabled to cut costs otherwise, or in the expectation of gaining some other business advantage. We shall consider in a moment what some of those cost savings or other advantages of "hedging" may be; what requires notice at this point is simply that making use of a futures contract as a temporary substitute for a merchandising contract is itself more or less costly. The cost must be kept very low, else handlers of the commodity will make little use of the futures market otherwise than for merchandising.

The cost of using a futures contract as a temporary substitute for a merchandising contract has two components,[32a] namely: (1)

[32a] Under certain circumstances bias in a futures price deserves to be considered as a third source of "hedging" cost; but its cost effect depends on the time interval over which the "hedge" is held, may be either positive or negative, according to the direction of the bias and whether the "hedge" is long or short; and if the "hedge" is placed as an alternative to making a forward merchandising transaction, the bias element to be included in the "hedging" cost is the *difference* between the bias in the futures price and the bias in the forward cash price, concerning which we know little.

[25]

the commission charge for executing the futures contract, and (2) the "transaction cost" arising from the fact that at any given moment, in any market, the price obtained on a selling order, placed for prompt execution, will ordinarily be lower than the price that would be paid on a similar buying order at that same moment. If such buying and selling orders happen to reach the market simultaneously, they result in a transaction in which the seller receives the same price that the buyer pays, but in the absence of such good fortune prompt execution is obtainable only at prices that differ more or less according to whether the order is for a sale or for a purchase.

In a futures market with a large volume of trading, where transactions occur in quick succession, the transaction cost of "hedging" tends to be quite small, perhaps about equal to the commission charge on a transaction. But in a futures market with very little trading, where long intervals commonly intervene between successive transactions, the average transaction cost of "hedging" may be several times as great as the commission charge, tending to discourage handlers of the commodity from using the futures contract for any purpose other than merchandising.

When effort to establish a new futures market ends in failure, as has been the case with a considerable proportion of the efforts of the Chicago Mercantile Exchange, there are three possible explanations to be considered, namely: (1) that the amount of potential use by handlers of the commodity was too small to provide the basic support for a successful futures market; (2) that some obstacle prevented the market from attracting enough speculation to produce the fluidity necessary to warrant much use of the futures contract for "hedging"; or (3) that, despite a potential for attracting enough of both business and speculative use to bring success, the market failed to surmount what may be called the "fluidity barrier".

A fluidity barrier is generated by the facts that the amount of business use and of speculative use of a futures market are interdependent, and that a quantum gap exists between the degree of fluidity needed to attract merchandising use of a futures market by handlers of the commodity, and that needed to attract wide use of the futures contract as a temporary substitute for merchandising contracts that will be made later. In consequence, a new futures market may have the potential of attracting enough of both business and speculative use to succeed, and yet fail of success because it fails to pass the fluidity barrier. Having attracted all the merchandising use that it can, and as much speculation as can be supported by that merchandising use, it still lacks the fluidity necessary to attract much "hedging"; the transaction cost of "hedging" remains too high.

As I read the record, growth of the onion futures market on the Chicago Mercantile Exchange remained stalled at the fluidity barrier for some three years after trading on it had been resumed following World War II. But in the 1949-50 season, with a crop that was moderately short, though considerably larger than that of two years earlier, prices to growers early in the season were nearly three times as high as they had been the year before. Many dealers thought the price too high (it ranged from $2.40 to $2.50 per 50 pound sack during October, and from $1.00 down to $.50 during the following April) and chose to "hedge" in the futures market. The increased business use of the market supported a corresponding increase in speculative use. It thus became a satisfactorily fluid market, and from that time on it prospered, until federal legislation forced its closing.[33]

The fact that there is more futures trading in the United States than in all other countries combined, seems attributable in large part to a combination of circumstances that have helped futures markets in this country to attract speculation. Even so, there have undoubtedly been instances in the United States in which an effort to establish a futures market has failed of success because of difficulty in attracting enough speculation. Any exchange which is not already operating a flourishing trade in futures faces two special obstacles if it tries to establish a new futures market. It does not have within its membership, and cannot immediately attract to itself, skilled professional floor traders to contribute to the fluidity of the market through their scalping trade; and

---

[33] Most of the statistical evidence underlying this interpretation may be found in Holbrook Working, "Price Effects of Futures Trading". *Food Research Institute Studies,* Vol. I, pp. 1-31, February 1960.

it encounters difficulty in persuading brokerage houses to supply their customers with price quotations and other information that could bring speculative trade to the new futures market.

Those were obstacles encountered by the Chicago Union Stockyards when that exchange, in 1930, sought to establish futures trading in live hogs. Everette Harris correctly appraises the failure of that effort, I believe, when he attributes it, on a later page, to lack of "public buyers". I would suspect also a lack of sufficient competent and competitive floor trading. An exchange that conducts futures trading in a number of different commodities can provide a more uniformly fluid market for any one of them than could an exchange dealing only in that one commodity. That is especially true for a commodity in which trading is light. To maintain a highly fluid market, scalpers must operate on an almost infinitesimally small profit margin, and a professional floor trader can afford to do that only if he does a great volume of business. That is not possible on a single-commodity exchange with a small volume of trading; but it is possible in a small futures market operating on a multi-commodity exchange, where a floor trader is not restricted to dealing only in that one commodity. Futures markets that are individually small can prosper modestly on a multi-commodity exchange whereas attempt to operate them separately would fail, for much the same reason that retail trade in a small and isolated town must be conducted in a "general store" rather than in a number of specialty shops.[34]

Examples can be cited which seem to prove that a futures market can, in fact, be operated successfully with a very small volume of business, and on an exchange with little or no other futures trading; but these exceptional cases do not invalidate the general rule. One sort of exception is that represented by the Milwaukee Grain Exchange; it is perhaps best characterized as a minor satellite of the Chicago Board of Trade, only narrowly missing classification as a "bucket shop". Another sort of exception is represented by the Seattle Grain Exchange, which is a

---

[34] Supporting evidence for the foregoing observations on floor trading may be found in Holbrook Working, "Tests of a Theory Concerning Floor Trading on Commodity Exchanges", *Food Research Institute Studies*, Vol. VII, Supplement, (1967), pp. 5-48.

truly independent exchange, concerned primarily with merchandising trade, that also maintained a wheat futures market for many years, up to 1960, with only a trifling volume of futures business. Its futures market was maintained partly in persistent hope that it would presently become self-sustaining, but perhaps more particularly for another reason. Much of the merchandising business done by members of the exchange was for deferred delivery, with dates and positions of delivery varying widely. Though transactions in the standardized futures contracts were few, prices on those transactions, and bids and offers in the absence of transactions, tended to keep closely in line with the prices on merchandising transactions. The futures market thus served, in effect, as a price-quotation service that translated the prices paid on unstandardized merchandising contracts into standardized contract terms.

3.

Enough has been said on earlier pages about the *need* for a futures market to attract "hedging" use. Here we proceed immediately to consider some of the reasons why handlers of a commodity choose to use the futures market otherwise than for merchandising. Some handlers of a commodity, like people in any other broad category of mature and active persons in the community, may, as individuals, choose to speculate, and to speculate in the commodity that they handle. I do not count that as a business use of the futures market. As a practical means for identifying business use of the futures market, otherwise than for merchandising, I accept the criterion that the futures contract be used as a temporary substitute for a merchandising contract that will be made later.[35]

---

[35] This criterion, in more specific form, was written into the Commodity Exchange Act as part of its definition of "hedging", as applied to processors and manufacturers, through an amendment in 1956 which made the Act read in part: "For the purposes of this paragraph, bona fide hedging transactions shall mean [among other things] . . . purchases of any commodity for future delivery on or subject to the rules of any board of trade to the extent that such purchases . . . shall not exceed such person's unfilled anticipated requirements for processing or manufacturing during a specified operating period not in excess of one year: *Provided,* That such purchase is made and liquidated in an orderly manner and in accordance with sound commercial practice . . ." (U.S. Department of Agri-

FUTURES TRADING IN LIVESTOCK

There is one quite general reason for any businessman's use of a futures market. The need for putting it foremost, with other reasons considered subsidiary, was brought to my attention by a remark of a grain merchant, Mr. Virgil A. Wiese, in an address that I chanced to hear. Grain merchants, he said, are not in business to avoid risk, but to make money. That remark deserves to be borne in mind as a warning that we should not too lightly assume that, if risk reduction can be shown, it is the sole reason for a businessman's use of the futures market; and we should not close our eyes to the possibility that businessmen may sometimes use a futures market with full recognition that they thereby take some added risk.

We should also bear in mind that a fairly intimate knowledge of the business may be needed in order to understand why a businessman uses a futures market. When I asked a flour-mill manager why millers *say* that they hedge to avoid risks, he promptly responded: "Because it is hard to explain the real reasons for mill 'hedging' to a person who doesn't understand the milling business".

A third fact to be noted at the outset is that there are two sides to the question, Why does a businessman "hedge". Sometimes we need to ask" Why does a businessman make temporary use of a futures contract, instead of entering immediately into a forward merchandising contract? And sometimes we need to ask: Why does a businessman want to buy or to sell now, for later delivery, instead of waiting to make a "spot" purchase or sale at the time when he wants to take delivery or to make delivery?

The former of these two subsidiary questions can be answered the more briefly, though even it has different answers in different

culture, Commodity Exchange Authority, Commodity Exchange Act, as Amended, Section 4a)

The temporary substitute criterion had previously been implicit in the Act's definition of hedging as applied to: (a) sales of futures by a producer, not exceeding ". . . the amount of such commodity such person is raising, or in good faith intends or expects to raise, within the next twelve months . . ."; (b) sale of futures ". . . against the products or by-products of such commodity owned or purchased [for later delivery] by such person . . ."; or (c) purchase of futures ". . . against the sale [on a forward merchandising contract] of any product or by-product of such commodity by such person".

But the Act does not at present recognize as "hedging" a purchase of futures by a merchant, to cover his "unfilled anticipated requirements" for merchandising.

circumstances. In some lines of processing (flour milling is an example) and in some kinds of merchandising, buying and selling decisions are simplified if purchases and offsetting sales can be made simultaneously, or nearly so. A futures market offers the opportunity for making a purchase or a sale at any time and with maximum convenience. Then the futures contract can be replaced by a merchandising contract as soon as a good opportunity arises.

In other circumstances, a commodity handler may want to make a forward sale, for example, but find no buyer on a merchandising contract who is willing to pay as much, quality and location considered, as speculators are willing to pay in the futures market. A sale on a futures contract is then made as a temporary substitute for a forward merchandising contract, not merely as a matter of convenience, but to get a better price.

In still other circumstances, the commodity handler may want to make a forward purchase or sale, and find no one willing to enter into the desired merchandising contract with him. A cattle feeder, for example, wanting to make a sales contract early in the feeding period, may be unable to find anyone who wants to buy his cattle, for delivery several months hence. In that case, use of a futures contract as a temporary substitute for a merchandising contract may be necessary, in the sense that it is the only means at hand for making a sale at that time, with delivery postponed.

To summarize, then, a futures contract may be used as a temporary substitute for a merchandising contract: (a) merely for the sake of convenience, allowing the contemplated merchandising contract to be made shortly afterward, but at leisure rather than under pressure; or (b) because the price on the futures market is more favorable, quality and location considered, than any price immediately available on a forward merchandising contract; or (c) from virtual necessity, because the futures market offers the only practical opportunity to make a forward sale, or purchase, at the desired time.

These different circumstances present different degrees of incentive to use of the futures market. The incentive tends to be greatest in a case like that of the cattle feeder, and may be so strong as to lead to the use of a futures contract that is a relatively poor substitute for the desired merchandising contract. Prior to the establishment of futures trading in live cattle, cattle feeders sometimes sold corn futures as a temporary substitute for a merchandising sale of their cattle. Any large change in cattle prices tends to be accompanied by a roughly similar change in corn prices, hence such a relatively poor substitute could be useful.

At the other extreme, use of a futures contract as a matter of convenience tends to occur only if the cost is slight and the futures contract a very good temporary substitute for a merchandising contract. Flour millers in the Pacific Coast states have had the choice of either using a wheat futures market in that area, which has tended to be expensive because the market lacked fluidity, or of using a mid-continent futures market, in which the futures contract was not a very good substitute for a West Coast merchandising contract (wheat prices in the two areas do not move in close day-to-day correspondence). In consequence, flour millers in Pacific Coast states have made little use of futures markets, [36] whereas mid-continent millers have been among the most consistent users of futures markets in any line of business.

Turn now to the question, why should a commodity handler want to buy or sell, on either a merchandising contract or some substitute contract, before he is ready to take delivery or to make delivery, as the case may be?

Probably the strongest reason for a producer, merchant, or warehouse operator to seek to make a sale is expectation of a large price decline between now and the time when he will want to make delivery; and probably the strongest reason for a merchant or processor to seek to make a forward purchase is expectation of a sharp price advance between now and the time when he will want delivery. The strength of the incentive depends on the degree of confidence with which the expectation is held. Many handlers of a commodity — most obviously, merchants operating over a wide territory, and large scale processors of the

---

[36] My information regarding the practice in recent years comes from trade sources. Out of 26 Pacific Coast mills that responded in a survey made by the Federal Trade Commission concerning hedging practice in 1915-16, only 3 reported any use of futures markets. (*Report on the Grain Trade*, Vol. VII, p. 44).

commodity, but also others who choose to keep well informed — can rightly place a good deal of confidence in their own price expectations, and can enhance their business profits by exercising judgment in the timing of purchases and sales.

When, for example, a merchant holding stocks of a commodity expects a price decline, and therefore sells futures, he ordinarily says that he sells to avoid risk. But if that sort of risk avoidance is to be considered the equivalent of taking out an insurance policy, the proper analogy is with a case of a man taking out life insurance immediately after being told by his doctor that he has no more than six months yet to live (the doctor's opinion might prove mistaken, just as the merchant's expectation might prove mistaken, hence uncertainty exists in each case).

Obviously it is important to distinguish between the two sorts of risk avoidance that a "hedger" may seek. If a business-man "hedges" regularly, making no effort to judge what price change is likely to occur, I shall call that "insurance-type hedging". If he "hedges" because he anticipates an adverse price change, I shall call that "anticipatory hedging".[37]

The difference between "anticipatory hedging" and speculation is, first, that in "anticipatory hedging" the purchase or sale of futures serves as a temporary substitute for a merchandising contract that will be made later — not more than a year later, according to the definition in the Commodity Exchange Act — whereas in the case of speculation no subsequent merchandising transaction is ordinarily contemplated. Secondly, "anticipatory hedging" seeks to profit from the exercise of price judgment without incurring any great amount of added risk — the risk assumed takes the place of an alternative risk that is avoided, — whereas speculation typically involves the assumption of risk with no offsetting avoidance of an alternative risk. Borderline cases arise if a business firm buys or sells futures too far in advance of the contemplated merchandising purchase or sale, but it remains important nevertheless to recognize that the exercise of price judgment through "anticipatory hedging", as ordinarily practiced, ought not to be classed as speculation.

---

[37] As here defined, "anticipatory hedging" includes what I have elsewhere called "selective hedging".

Perhaps, I have been asking the reader to depend too much on unaided imagination in an effort to visualize "hedging" under different circumstances. Table 2 presents some statistics on use of a futures market by handlers of the commodity that can help toward visualizing different situations realistically. The data are a breakdown, by occupation, of some of the statistics previously given in Table 1 as totals for all handlers of the commodity. The statistics are for onions because that is the only commodity, with the possible exception of potatoes, for which so much information on open contracts, by occupation of the handler, is available.

I have not been able to visualize any circumstances under which an onion grower would have occasion to *buy* onion futures as a temporary substitute for a merchandising contract to be made later; consequently I regard all, or nearly all[38] of the recorded long holdings of futures by onion growers as reflecting speculation rather than business use of the futures market. A grower who sometimes speculated and sometimes "hedged" would be likely to have his account classed by the reporting commission merchant as a speculative account, even at a time when he had only a short position, classifiable under the Commodity Exchange Act as "hedging". It is possible, therefore, that the greater part of the short positions of growers that are shown in Table 2 under the heading " 'speculative' accounts" deserve to

---

[38] It is necessary to qualify because a long position in one delivery month may have been acquired as partial offset to a previously acquired short position in another delivery month, leaving the "hedger" with a "spread" position, to be closed out subsequently. For example, an onion grower may have sold 40 carlots (an amount slightly less than the average short position of reportedly hedging growers on August 31) on the first trading day of July, six weeks before harvest, and may have made the sale in the high priced February future. Then on August 20 he may have sold 5 carlots of harvested onions, spot, and immediately "lifted his hedge" to that extent by purchasing the lower priced November future. Suppose, then, that he waited until late October to close out the resulting spread position; the series of transactions would have proved highly advantageous, as may be seen from the following price quotations (closing prices per 50-pound bag from Chicago Mercantile Exchange *Yearbook*);

Delivery Month	July 2	Aug. 20	October 19
February 1957	$2.45	$1.40	$1.03
November 1956	1.94	1.08	.79
Difference	.51	.32	.24

HISTORY AND DEVELOPMENT

Table 2. Numbers of Onion Handlers Holding Futures Contracts
and Numbers of Carlots Held, by Class of Handler,
Classification of Account, and Date, 1956*

Class of onion handler and date	"Speculative" accounts			"Hedging" accounts		
	No.	Carlots		No.	Carlots	
		Long	Short		Long	Short
Growers						
May 31	15	266	135	18	22	234
Aug. 31	47	456	354	29	101	1,271
Oct. 31	46	351	329	30	53	1,255
Dec. 31	59	346	137	19	49	887
Grower; shippers and dealers						
Aug. 31	24	282	24	7	10	731
Oct. 31	18	281	16	4	5	716
Dec. 31	23	352	260	7	19	779
Terminal market merchants						
May 31	25	360	254	13	52	646
Aug. 31	74	1,033	188	22	108	1,179
Oct. 31	103	1,180	332	19	157	1,051
Dec. 31	104	1,326	465	26	148	812
Brokers (cash onions)						
May 31	0	0	0	2	5	1
Aug. 31	13	93	0	2	30	2
Oct. 31	11	114	0	0	0	0
Dec. 31	8	51	0	0	0	0
Grocer organizations						
May 31	6	30	0	0	0	0
Aug. 31	9	43	0	1	40	0
Oct. 31	18	78	0	0	0	0
Dec. 31	8	15	23	0	0	0
Processors						
May 31	0	0	0	0	0	0
Aug. 31	2	34	0	1	175	0
Oct. 31	2	20	0	1	124	0
Dec. 31	2	29	0	1	62	0

* Data from Commodity Exchange Authority, *Surveys of Open Contracts* (mimeo.):
Classification as "speculative" or "hedging" made by futures commission merchant
carrying the account, presumably in an effort to comply with the definition of
"hedging" in the Commodity Exchange Act.

be regarded as "hedging". In commenting on "hedging" by
onion growers I take these into account, as well as the short
positions specifically reported as "hedging".

From sometime in April until late summer, freshly harvested
onions move quickly from the fields to the consumer, first from
areas in Texas where the harvest is earliest, and subsequently

from areas with progressively later harvests. Finally comes what is called the late summer crop, grown in areas with a cold climate, harvested mainly during September and October[39], and mostly placed in storage, for shipment during later months, until March or April. Storage is almost entirely on the premises of the grower, in what is called common storage, with only the refrigeration provided by nature. Growers holding short positions, even as early as May 31, appear to have been nearly all concerned with production for the late summer crop.[40]

Short positions held by growers as early as May 31, 369 carlots, are possibly all classifiable as representing "insurance-type hedging", on the supposition that those growers, attracted during April by futures prices of $1.60 to $1.80 per 50 pound bag (November future), had decided to raise onions instead of some alternative crop and had thereupon "hedged" by selling in the futures market. By August 31, total short positions held by growers had increased from the 369 carlots held on May 31 to 1,625. Some parts of that increase may have represented "insurance-type hedging", but most of it, I suspect, arose from "anticipatory hedging", motivated by opinions that the price after harvest was unlikely to be so high as it was currently. The price of the November future went above $2.00 on one day in June and on most days during July; but it declined precipitously during August to a low of $1.01 on the final day of the month.

Growers who held a short position in futures at harvest time, unless financially pressed, would have tended in most instances to seek to sell their harvested onions at times when they could get a price that appeared favorable in relation to the futures price; because they intended to lift their "hedge" at the same

---

[39] Statistics of onion production are compiled for three categories, according to time of maturity of the crop, namely, "spring", "early summer", and "late summer", and the latter is taken as August-September. But actual harvest in the more northerly producing areas extends through October to such an extent that November was taken as the first month for deliveries on futures contracts. And onions harvested as early as August, though in considerable part stored, do not keep well in common storage beyond about December.

[40] The published classification of contracts by geographic area gives no breakdown by occupation of the trader; total short positions of all traders in states where onions are harvested before late summer amounted to only 66 carlots on May 31, as compared with the total of 369 carlots for "growers" alone on that date.

[36]

time that they sold the cash onions, they would give attention to that price relation rather than to the price itself. During October the February future held about 24 cents above the price for November delivery, and the price of the March future, 11 cents higher yet. Onions lose weight in storage, hence the incentive to postpone sale of stored onions until later in the storage season was not so strong as these price differences might suggest, but an incentive was present and would have tended to influence any grower holding a "hedged" supply of onions.

The second category in Table 2 appears to have been intended to provide information on use of the futures market by dealers in onions at country points, not growers; in the CEA publications, the data appear under the heading "onion shippers and dealers (in growing areas)". But onion growing in the northern producing areas tends to be one-crop farming, leaving the grower with little or nothing to do on the land for several months after the crop is harvested. Some enterprising growers occupy themselves after harvest as "onion shippers", selling their own onions, and onions purchased from their neighbors, to terminal market merchants. Such a grower-shipper might see no reason to keep two accounts with his futures commission merchant, one designated as connected with his business as a grower and the other connected with his business as a shipper, and if he kept only one such account it might be reported to the CEA as that of an onion shipper. Now onion shippers and dealers at country points, as such, have little occasion to hedge, inasmuch as they do little or no storing of onions; but we see in Table 2 that the short "hedging" positions reported for what I call "grower-shippers and dealers" averaged, after May 31, more than twice as large per account as did the corresponding positions of "onion growers". I infer that these short "hedging" positions should be interpreted as chiefly or wholly "hedging" by growers, and that they averaged large per account because those onion growers who engage also in the shipping business tend to be particularly large scale growers.

Long positions classed as speculative seem to me necessarily so classed in the case of "grower-shippers" as well as in that of "growers". Short positions of grower-shippers, however classed

[37]

in the table, seem to me to deserve the presumption that they were held as temporary substitutes for merchandising contracts that would be made later; but whether they represented "insurance-type hedging" or "anticipatory hedging" is open to as much question in the case of a "grower-shipper" as in that of a "grower".

Terminal market merchants whose accounts were classed as "hedging" accounts, and who were net short in the futures market, may reasonably be presumed to have held those net short positions against onions that they had purchased, some of those onions, perhaps, being still held by the grower for later shipment. Whether such holding of futures by a merchant should be classed as "insurance-type hedging" or "anticipatory hedging" might have been determinable at the time either through interview with the merchant or from study of his past practice. If he had a record of sometimes "hedging" and sometimes not, there would be grounds for suspecting that in this instance he had thought a price decline likely and had "hedged" for that reason. We shall later encounter an apparently authoritative statement indicating that onion futures were little used for "insurance-type hedging".

Any terminal market merchant who held a net long position may almost certainly be regarded as having held the futures contracts as a temporary substitute for merchandising purchases that he would make later — probably not more than a few weeks later, inasmuch as the average size of the long positions classed as "speculative" never exceeded 14 carlots per account. On that ground his use of the futures market might be regarded as "anticipatory hedging". But, I suppose, that the price at which a merchant can sell at any given time is very closely dependent on the price at which he might buy at that time. If so, the risk that he incurs through forward buying, whether in the futures market or otherwise, is not offset by a corresponding risk avoided; on that ground, any forward buying that he does might be classed as speculation. Yet there is still another factor to be considered. The nature of the merchant's business is such that he must buy some days or weeks before he sells, and carry stocks either in storage or in transit. Suppose that he must buy, on the average, at least two weeks in advance of sale and that, thinking a price advance likely, he bought futures in an amount equal to two additional weeks of sales; because risk of price change increases approximately as the square root of the time interval involved, buying twice as far ahead has not doubled his risk, but has increased it by only about 40 percent.

The long positions of terminal market merchants in the futures market are therefore peculiarly difficult to classify. I shall call them "speculative", but put the term in quotation marks to indicate doubt whether they ought to be so classed. They constituted 34 percent of all long positions classed by the CEA as "speculative" on October 31, and 37 percent at the end of December.

The most noteworthy figures in the remainder of Table 2 are the long "hedging" positions of one onion processor, starting with 175 carlots long on August 31 and diminishing progressively in amount on successive reporting dates. These seem clearly to present an example of "anticipatory hedging", the size of the futures position being reduced as purchases were made on merchandising contracts. Such use of a futures market was not effectively recognized as "hedging" under the Commodity Exchange Act until September 28, 1956, but the reporting futures commission merchant evidently counted it as such on August 31. The two processors whose long positions were classed as "speculative" presumably held their accounts with futures commission merchants who took a different view of the proper classification of such accounts. The fact that so few processors are shown as making use of the onion futures market is attributable at least in part to need by processors for onions quite different from the yellow globe variety represented by the futures contract, the prices of which tend to move quite differently than the prices of yellow globe onions, and partly to a long established practice by onion processors of contracting for their supplies in advance of planting, with growers who could be counted on to deliver onions of the desired kind and quality.[41]

---

[41] How general that practice has been I do not know; I encountered it in the one instance in which I inquired into an onion processor's practice.

[39]

FUTURES TRADING IN LIVESTOCK

Probably no two futures markets are alike in the degree to which they draw business from different classes of users. The onion futures market, which we have been led to take as a concrete example because of the availability of statistics on open contracts, by occupational classes, for a number of well spaced successive dates, drew an unusually large proportion of its short "hedging" from producers. But it was unusual in that respect only because most futures markets have dealt in commodities that are easily stored, and can be stored most economically in commercially operated warehouses. Authors of papers that follow will be found to expect the futures markets for live cattle and for hogs to also draw the major portion of their short hedging from producers of the commodity.

The extent to which futures markets draw long "hedging" from processors or manufacturers varies greatly from one commodity to another. Where there is a great deal of such long "hedging" it is not necessarily "anticipatory hedging" from the standpoint of the firm holding the futures contracts — in the wheat market, long hedging by flour mills is simply a reflection of anticipatory forward buying of flour by bakeries.

Very little information is available on the extent to which dealers in different commodities take long positions in the futures market. Presumably dealers who normally hold substantial stocks of the commodity, as onion dealers in terminal markets do not, tend much less than did such onion merchants to take long positions in the futures market; they can "speculate", if that is the proper word for it, simply by refraining from "hedging" the stocks that they hold.

In the case of a commodity that is stored in large quantities at central points, giving rise to the development of warehousing as a specialized business, there tends to emerge also a distinctive sort of "hedging", if a futures market is available. To the extent that the warehouser owns the commodity that he stores, his basic operating decision is whether to buy for storage or not. Given opportunity to sell forward, either on forward merchandising contracts or in a futures market, a decision to buy for storage tends to be made on the basis on the "carrying charge" reflected in the difference between the current price at which a forward sale can be made and the corresponding current spot price. No question arises as to whether to sell forward or not, it being taken for granted that any spot purchase will be offset by a forward sale in equal amount either in the futures market or on a forward merchandising contract. If the choice is to sell in the futures market, that decision may be taken for any of the three reasons given earlier for such a choice, namely: convenience, a more favorable price, or absence of any immediate opportunity to make a suitable forward merchandising sale.

4.

Near the end of this volume Don Paarlberg emphasizes the need for public understanding of the usefulness of futures markets. That need can be critical. In 1893, a bill that would have put an end to all futures trading in the United States only narrowly escaped enactment by the 52nd Congress. A similar bill considered by the 53rd Congress was passed by the House, but failed in the Senate.[42] During the next sixty years, so far as I know, no attack on futures trading came so close as that to success, but in 1958 a more limited attack succeeded; in that year any further futures trading in onions was prohibited by federal legislation.

If education in the usefulness of futures markets is to be as effective as it should be, it must be directed in part at correcting prevalent misconceptions. Without such direction, an attempt to defend futures markets is like trying to defend a military position by random firing in the dark, without knowledge of the position of the enemy. Critical prevalent misconceptions regarding futures markets are nowhere more clearly revealed than in the committee hearings that preceded congressional action on the legislation to prohibit futures trading in onions — hearings that led committees of both the Senate and the House to recommend, unanimously so far as the records show, that futures trading in onions should be prohibited.

Although the voluminous record of the committee hearings

---

[42] Emery, H.C., *Speculation on the Stock and Produce Exchanges of the United States* (New York, 1896), pp. 219-23.

includes excellent presentations of the case for futures trading as well as the arguments against it, our concern at this point is with the line of reasoning, and the statements of fact, or supposed fact, that led the committees to decide against the futures market.[43] These may be summarized as follows:

(1) In the absence of a futures market the price of a commodity is determined by natural operation of the law of supply and demand; with a futures market, speculation becomes a major price influence, causing unwarranted price movement such as would not otherwise occur.

(2) Much speculation in futures is mere gambling, by people with little or no knowledge of the commodity situation; and much speculation is "in-and-out", the speculator holding any one position for only a brief time.

(3) "Hedging" is useful to handlers of the commodity only as a means of risk avoidance; it serves that purpose well, and is beneficial to the public, only if it is practiced systematically, as "insurance-type hedging".

(4) There was little systematic hedging in onion futures, hedgers have tended ". . . to hedge only partially and to place and remove their hedges sporadically, with changing appraisal of market conditions . . . The average producer of onions does little, if any, direct hedging in the futures market."[44]

The final statements above, quoted from the testimony of the Administrator of the Commodity Exchange Authority, Mr. Rodger R. Kauffman, deserves immediate comment. His statement that most "hedging" had been sporadic, which I assume to have been founded on good evidence, was made in a context that indicated belief on his part that such "hedging" failed to serve an economically useful purpose. His statement that the average onion producer did little if any direct hedging may

---

[43] A particularly full presentation of evidence on both sides appears in U.S. 85th Congress, 2nd Session, Senate, *Hearing Before the Committee on Agriculture and Forestry*, March 20, 21, 24, 25, and 26, 1958. An earlier subcommittee hearing, held under a chairman who frankly admitted his bias against the futures market, seems to me to reveal especially clearly the line of reasoning that proved most influential with the congressional committees. The transcript of that hearing is cited in a footnote below.

[44] U.S. 85 Congress, 1st Session, Senate, *Hearing before a Subcommittee of the Committee on Agriculture and Forestry*, Aug. 12, 1957, pp. 29, 30.

be technically defensible on the ground that the number of onion producers classed as hedgers (Table 2 above) was rather small in relation to the total number of onion growers in the country; but it tends to give an impression at variance with the fact that persons classified purely as growers (not counting the grower-shippers) are credited with about the same amount of hedging, in the aggregate, as is shown for all terminal market merchants using the futures market. Growers and grower-shippers together were credited in the statistics with more "hedging" than all other users of the market combined.

The fallacy of proposition (1) above lies in its neglect of the fact that the price of a commodity, of which stocks are held, cannot be determined by an impersonal economic law; it is determined by human judgments, essentially speculative, regarding what those stocks can be sold for at a later time. The existence of a futures market, while allowing some people to speculate in the commodity who would not otherwise be able to do so, also allows those holders of the commodity who distrust their own price judgments, to escape from what would otherwise be a need to "speculate".

Proposition (2) is a double proposition. Its first part depends for its persuasiveness on an implied assumption that holders of stocks of the physical commodity, in the absence of a futures market, are none of them ill informed and essentially gambling on price prospects. The second part, implying that the only useful speculation in futures is that which involves holding positions for extended periods, ignores the fact that price prospects for a stored commodity are subject to frequent change, giving reason for alert observers of the economic situation to often change their positions in the market, thereby promoting price adjustment to the new situation.

Proposition (3) rests on a narrow and oversimplified concept of "hedging", promoted by writers with little knowledge of the diversity of ways in which handlers of a commodity can use a futures market to advantage, depending on special characteristics of the line of business in which they are engaged. Because textbook explanations of "hedging" have identified it almost exclusively with what I have called "insurance-type hedging", it may

[43]

be necessary in discussion of the economic usefulness of futures markets to abandon use of the term "hedging", and to speak instead of "use of the futures market by handlers of the commodity". Perhaps the most serious consequence of widespread acceptance of the narrow definition of "hedging" is its implication, widely accepted, that handlers of the commodity, through their use of a futures market, cease to influence the price, and leave price determination largely in the hands of speculators in the futures market. The fact may be that handlers of a commodity often use the futures market in such a way as to increase the extent to which the price is influenced by well informed handlers of the commodity.

Once misconceptions have been sufficiently dealt with, the chief merits of futures markets, from the public standpoint, can be presented rather briefly and simply. They may be stated under three heads, beginning with what I regard as the least important, as follows:

A. Effect on price variability.

Commodities for which a futures market can exist are inevitably subject to frequent and sometimes large price changes owing to changes in economic conditions and prospects. Whether the existence of a futures market tends to result in less price variation, or more variation, than would otherwise occur cannot be demonstrated on the basis of economic reasoning alone. The evidence from statistical studies appears to me to be conclusive on only one point, namely, that the average amount of seasonal variation in the price tends to be less in the presence of a futures market than in its absence. There is much statistical evidence indicating that selling pressure by producers at times of seasonal surplus causes less price depression in the presence of a futures market than in its absence; and there is no evidence, so far as I know, that points toward a contrary conclusion.

Reliable statistical evidence comparing price variability (other than average seasonal variation) with and without a futures market is scanty, partly owing to a scarcity of statistical studies that have used sufficiently sensitive statistical tests, but largely because there have been few opportunities to make statistical comparisons under conditions that allowed reasonably confident judgment that an observed difference in price variability within the year was attributable to existence of the futures market rather than to some other change in conditions. One study, made under particularly favorable circumstances in the latter respect, has indicated fairly clearly that futures trading tended to moderate price fluctuations, through diminishing the amplitudes of price variations caused by changes in supply prospects. A futures market offers rich reward for early recognition of any change in supply prospects, and if a prospective shortage, for example, is recognized early, the price advance that is needed to effect market equilibrium is less than that which becomes necessary if recognition of the shortage is delayed until late.[45]

B. Usefulness to handlers of the commodity.

Futures markets can exist, as we have seen above, only on the basis of usefulness to handlers of the commodity. The amount of business done on a futures market varies from commodity to commodity, and from time to time for any one commodity, in fairly close proportion to the amount of business that futures markets attract from handlers of the commodity. The benefits derived by producers, merchants, warehousers, or processors from their use of a futures market differ according to the nature of the business and other circumstances. One benefit that can often be gained is a considerable reduction in risk, along with avoidance of need to try to anticipate likely price changes.

But it is not necessarily in the public interest that businessmen handling the commodity should hedge routinely, thus avoiding major participation in the price-forming process; if all handlers of a particular commodity did that, price-formation for that commodity would be left almost wholly in the hands of speculators on the futures market, who might or might not be as well informed, on balance, as businessmen handling the commodity. And many businessmen, from producers to processors, consider it good business on their part to exercise price judgment in the

---

[45] The statistical evidence which I interpret thus appeared originally in Holbrook Working, "Price Effects of Futures Trading", *Food Research Institute Studies*, Vol. 1, pp. 17-23, 1960; it was summarized briefly and supplemented by some additional evidence in H. Working, "Futures Markets under Renewed Attack", *Food Research Institute Studies*, Vol. 4, pp. 18-20 (1963).

timing of their sales or their purchases, or both. For such businessmen, a futures market offers the advantage of avoiding conflict between the dictates of price judgment and other business considerations.

Examples of the usefulness of a futures market in avoidance of conflict between different business considerations can be drawn from any line of business involving the handling of a commodity. A cattle feeder has little choice as to the time when he moves his cattle from feedlot to market; but by judicious use of the futures market he can in effect time the sale within a span of many months, in accordance with his price judgment. A merchant may be under the necessity of accumulating stocks when producers want to sell, lest he lose established business connections and good will; but through appropriate use of the futures market, he can, in effect, time his purchases as price judgment dictates. A fruit canner must have sugar when the fruit arrives for packing, and cannot economically accumulate large stocks in advance; but through use of the futures market, he can, in effect, buy the needed sugar well in advance, when he considers the price advantageous. Such uses of a futures market are not only advantageous to any user with good price judgment; they tend also to promote better adjustment of the price to existing supply conditions and prospects than would occur if handlers of the commodity were more restricted in their exercise of price judgment.

C. Openly competitive pricing.

Commodity markets in which *merchandising* transactions are executed in open competitive bargaining have virtually disappeared in the United States, and elsewhere in the commercially developed world. Where they continue to exist, in the United States at least, only a tiny fraction of total merchandising trade occurs on them, and in a large proportion of such instances they are maintained solely for the purpose of providing price quotations on a few publicly executed transactions. The representativeness of these transactions is then open to question.

With virtually all merchandising trade carried on through private negotiation, a large firm, with extensive private sources of market information, has substantial competitive advantage over any small firm, possessed of only limited information on the current attitudes of prospective buyers and sellers. Producers, for the most part, sell in a local market where, as always, there tends to be only limited competition between buyers; and the producers of most farm products today lack the guidance of a reliable price on a central merchandising market to aid them in their negotiations with buyers. They can know, through market news reports, what prices other producers, in a similarly disadvantaged position, are receiving, but that may tend more toward forcing them to accept a comparatively low price than toward helping them to bargain for a better price.

That, at least, is the prevalent situation today in the absence of a futures market for the commodity. But in the presence of a futures market, with its open and highly competitive bargaining, the absence of an open competitive merchandising market does not matter. Prices on the futures market record accurately the current balance of market opinion. Properly understood, they help the bargaining position of producers, small merchants, and small processors even more than would an open and competitive merchandising market that recorded only prices on spot transactions.

In one of the papers that follow Henry Bakken devotes several paragraphs to the fact that a futures market tends to counter the effects of oliogopsonic conditions in the pricing of a commodity; but elsewhere in the literature there is little reference to that merit of a futures market. During the three-quarters of a century that has passed since the traditional lines of argument in favor of futures markets were laid down, marketing conditions have changed. Today, the fact that futures trading provides central market prices established in open competitive bargaining may deserve to be regarded as the chief merit of futures markets from the public standpoint.

Trading Floor — Chicago Mercantile Exchange

History of the Chicago Mercantile Exchange

by

Everette B. Harris

President — Chicago Mercantile Exchange

While commodity futures trading is a relatively modern development, mankind has always made attempts to benefit in the future from production in the present. As Time Magazine remarked, referring to the Old Testament's story of Joseph, "After, all, when the seven fat years ended in Egypt and the seven lean years began, wasn't Joseph the only man with grain stacked in his barns?"

In modern history, geography had much to do with Chicago becoming a world center of commodity trading. The Midwest's productive capacities, the processing facilities in Chicago and nearby cities, and the transportation network of roads, rivers, canals and the lakes all combined to create a grain exchange, more than 120 years ago.

PRODUCTION SEASONAL

During the last half of the 19th century, a fast-growing nation was at the mercy of alternating periods of scarcity and plenty. Cold storage facilities were primitive, markets were disorganized, and major production was seasonal.

FUTURES TRADING IN LIVESTOCK

In the case of butter, for example, a Chicago Product Exchange was formed in 1874 which established grades and rules of trading. Kegs of butter were individually smelled and tasted on the spot, and a price was agreed on. Some butter produced in the warm months was heavily salted and stored in basements for later use. The Chicago Butter and Egg Board was organized in 1898, and by 1915 the Board had developed 28 rules governing butter grading.

C.M.E. FOUNDED

Chicago Mercantile Exchange records show that after World War I, the industry leaders banded together to form an organization to permit public participation under carefully supervised commodity trading regulations. In 1919, early planners including S. E. Davis, O. W. Olson, W. S. Moore and C. E. McNeil established the Chicago Mercantile Exchange. The initial day of trading was on December 1. During the first 45-minute session, 3 cars were traded; a total of 8 cars were traded during that first week.

Early trading was in an old building at LaSalle and Lake streets. After 5 years, the Exchange governors decided that North Franklin Street would be a valuable property in the years ahead, and property was secured at the northwest corner of Franklin and Washington.

On September 16, 1926, Exchange officials quickly vetoed architects' proposals that the new building's elevator shafts be located in the central part of the trading floor. On November 2, members were told "it has definitely been decided that the new home of the Chicago Mercantile Exchange at Washington and Franklin will be 17 stories high. The first nine floors will be built with a steel frame and the remaining eight floors of concrete." The idea of using concrete was to limit construction costs. Those wishing to make the entire building concrete were defeated because heavy pillars would have been required throughout the trading floor in order to support the building's weight.

SOMETHING NEW!

While members traded butter, eggs, and ideas in their old stand, construction got under way when $2,600,000 in bonds were subscribed. The plans specified that, "The Exchange trading floor should occupy the second floor. It was to be reached by a marble stairway and six elevators. The area provided was approximately 75 by 125 feet; a high ceiling and no pillars or posts intervened to obstruct vision of the entire trading floor. The third floor included a studio for radio; it was anticipated that we would do our own broadcasting from the building."

Plans for the trading floor anticipated a form of pit trading similar to that being used on the Chicago Board of Trade. The blackboard system was not entirely satisfactory because it was difficult to install boards which would expedite trade during hectic periods when trades assumed tidal proportions. Shortly after construction ended, the new building was dedicated with an impressive ceremony and banquet held on April 25, 1928, at which humorist Will Rogers was an honored guest and speaker.

For a number of years, business was conducted in a relatively unhurried fashion. Most desks had a single phone; clerks and runners were almost unheard of, and members gathered in front of blackboards on standards. The world grew more complex, and so did life at the Chicago Mercantile Exchange. Post-depression years saw the Exchange building sold to its present owners, the Material Service Corporation; later to Henry Crown & Co. The trading floor was "turned around" to face double-decked boards covering the East wall and much of the South and North walls. A new ceiling with built-in lighting and air conditioning was formed to cover the ornate ceiling and chandeliers originally installed. In the early 1960's, new desks and chairs were provided, and a new floor encased the complicated wiring necessary as leads to hundreds of telephones, to time clocks, and to sending and receiving machines.

Prior to World War II, the Chicago Mercantile Exchange was synonymous with butter and eggs, and virtually all futures trading was dormant during the war. Principal butter and egg traders of the roaring twenties began to disappear and were virtually nonexistent in the fabulous forties. Technological changes had transformed the production and distribution of butter and storage eggs from seasonally produced commodities with classical production and price cycles to basically new and different products in their production, price and distribution patterns. The economic necessity of hedging markets provided by a futures market had greatly diminished. Futures trading in storage butter had almost disappeared and trading in eggs became tenuous.

Partially successful efforts were made by members to modify rules relative to egg futures trading by shifting from refrigerator to shell eggs. That is, trading in fresh eggs began. Trading in storage eggs continued, but at a discount. This discount continually increased from year to year until presently hedgers and speculators are trading very heavily in strictly fresh eggs with storage eggs nondeliverable. Thus, the Exchange tried to keep abreast of changing times in the egg industry. Members are proud that the highly efficient, mechanized, and modernized egg industry uses the updated egg futures contract as a helpful pricing tool. It is used by producers and handlers both for long and short hedging, for forward pricing, and for price information.

So much for eggs. It became apparent that members could not continue to subsist economically on eggs alone. Necessity is the mother of invention. Beginning in the early fifties and until the present time, Exchange members have vigorously researched, tested, and promoted many new contracts for futures trading. Most have been agricultural commodities but some non-agricultural commodities were also formulated. Some have succeeded and some have failed, but fear of failure has not impeded progress. The commodities which have fallen by the wayside in futures trading include onions, scrap iron, frozen shrimp, frozen broilers, hides, and apples. Successful markets have been established in frozen pork bellies, Idaho potatoes, live hogs, strictly fresh eggs, and the most exciting current futures — live beef cattle. The Chicago Mercantile Exchange is the second largest and fastest growing market in the world today. For the first time in history, August, 1969, saw the Chicago Mercantile Exchange the leader in volume among the major U. S. Commodity Exchanges.

The following tabulations are from the monthly report by the Association of Commodity Exchange Firms Inc. in New York.

Table 3

COMMODITY EXCHANGES WITH GREATEST PERCENTAGE OF U.S.
VOLUME — BASED ON TRANSACTIONS COMPLETED IN AUGUST, 1969

	Percentage of total transactions	Number of contracts traded in August '69	Number of contracts traded in August '68
1. Chicago Mercantile Exchange	39.1%	337,690	139,956
2. Chicago Board of Trade	38.9%	336,264	416,061
3. N.Y. Coffee & Sugar Exchange	7.0%	60,727	35,961
4. Commodity Exchange, Inc.	5.0%	44,088	45,435
5. N.Y. Cocoa	4.0%	35,570	35,314
6. N.Y. Mercantile Exchange	2.0%	16,115	49,312
Total of other exchanges	4.0%	32,690	70,231
TOTAL	100.0%	863,144	792,270

Table 4

GREATEST INCREASE IN VOLUME OF SPECIFIC COMMODITIES DURING
MONTH OF AUGUST (NUMBER OF CONTRACTS)
AUGUST, 1969 vs AUGUST, 1968

Commodity & Exchange listed on	1968	1969	Increase
1. Cattle — CME	16,521	123,519	106,998
2. Pork Bellies — CME	103,791	160,632	56,841
3. Fresh Eggs — CME	16,454	45,034	28,850
4. World Sugar — NYC&S	35,235	59,062	23,827
5. Corn — CBOT	111,453	128,881	17,482
6. Broilers — CBOT	507	14,562	14,055
7. Soybean Oil — CBOT	21,976	32,855	10,879
8. Copper — Com. Exchg.	1,005	10,851	9,846
9. Hogs — CME	676	7,256	6,580
10. Steers — CBOT	1,534	5,089	3,555

True, the Chicago Mercantile Exchange has grown, adapted, and changed with the times. But in many ways it has not changed since its founding fathers laid out its goals, purposes, and standards as shown below:

"The proposed business and objects for which said corporation is formed is to make for the benefit of its members daily quotations of market prices on butter, eggs and produce, and to furnish general information to its members regarding the markets for such commodities, and to furnish a convenient place where its members may buy and sell such commodities, and to facilitate the speedy adjustment of business disputes."

[53]

Today, because of the modern promotion methods aggressively used by the Chicago Mercantile Exchange and by its members, we can say "Business is 'show business' but it must be done with integrity." With leadership goes responsibility, and increasingly higher and higher standards have been set and met. Yet, as the French say "the more things change, the more they remain the same."

In 1926, Florence Sherman, secretary at the Exchange, wrote a poem for the "Exchange News" which read in part as follows:

HOW IT LOOKS AT THE DOOR

One by one, they trickle in,
Some just quiet, some with din,
Some with lightly tripping toe,
Some with faces filled with woe.

And now approaches eleven o'clock,
The markets cease to roll and rock,
Hundreds of cars are bought and sold,
The record of which the world is told.

The bell has rung the close at last,
The sound of conflict is ebbing fast,
The settlement price is posted too,
It cannot suit each one of you.

Now one by one they trickle out,
Some are sure, some are in doubt,
Some will gain, and some will pay,
Ah, well, tomorrow's another day.

And so the story goes in 1969 — the Golden Anniversary of the Chicago Mercantile Exchange.

Part II

Basic Concepts Pertinent to Futures Trading
In Meats and Livestock

Home on the Range

ADAPTION OF FUTURES TRADING TO LIVE CATTLE

By
Henry H. Bakken
University of Wisconsin

Some of the most remarkable milestones along the highways of business evolution paralleling those of the industrial revolution were the social innovations which antedated that period by some centuries. These were the coinage of money, the abolition of slavery, private property ownership, the negotiable contract, the bill of exchange, and the corporate organization, among others. In my estimation, the concept of trading in futures should be accorded a place in history equal to any of these. It might even be one of greater significance. The technique of trading in futures deserves this recognition because it is a very novel idea still not fully comprehended by many. It serves to accentuate the preceding social inventions of mankind implementing and bringing them into play in all the free markets of the world.

Through the use of futures contracts, traders have succeeded in reducing all the divergent characteristics of the things bought and sold to a common denominator. The common denominator, of course, is the equitable legal rights to goods, service, and properties. McLeod, the astute Scottish banker, was one of the first writers to maintain that, in the market place, it is not physical commodities that are bought and sold; it is the legal rights to these things. This trenchant observation was made in

1881, long after businessmen had initiated contractural obligations as a means of practical expediency.

The period in which a new futures contract is launched can be critical. Some futures contracts have been formulated prematurely and failed because those concerned were not ready for change. Similarly, some contracts have been offered belatedly with indifferent success. In forming the live cattle futures in 1964, it appears from subsequent events that the timing was propitious. The officials of the Chicago Mercantile Exchange are to be commended for their foresight, whether they were clairvoyant or just lucky.

Another aspect of time that has a bearing on futures relates to it as a factor in the determination of values. All prices usually have three dimensions. Scarcity was the first to be recognized possibly because it was the most obvious — shades of Malthus. Utility came into focus next as men conceived new uses for the resources around them. This process goes on apace. The time dimension, third in the series that was recognized, was much more elusive — nevertheless, it is the most important. The whole area of market activity of any real consequence extends from the present instant on into the future because all ownership lies in the future. Men live in expectation of the amenities of life. This idea has been expressed in a classical way as follows: "Man emerges from the past, acts in the present, and lives for the future." When prices are projected into the future, as it is done in a futures market, it enables men to plan their activities, both productive and pleasurable, with a higher degree of certainty. Value judgements based on scarcity and utility are generally inspired by the attributes of corporeal goods, but these are ephemeral.

In soliciting advice from some of my friends in the preparation of this paper, one of them took a dim view concerning the probable success of any futures contract based on livestock. As a matter of fact, he entertained doubts about their efficacy for all animal products in general. It is recognized that futures trading in various kinds of grain has been outstandingly successful. It is accepted as an indispensable institution facilitating distribution. Apparently it has attained a status of permanency in the market system prevailing in this country. Yet, with some humility, we must recognize this same procedure was well established at one time in Canada, England, France, Germany and a number of other countries of the world. In Europe, Asia, and elsewhere, Commodity Exchanges have been supplanted by state trading or totalitarian intervention. This transition gives emphasis to the old axiom that, "There is nothing permanent except change."

My friend's critical attitude toward futures trading in livestock, of course, represents the traditional point of view concerning the limited applicability of trading in futures. The earlier writers on the subject contended that the technique of selling futures contracts is circumscribed in its application to a limited number of commodities. The reasons given in support of this view were presumably derived by some process of rationalization, but their premises proved faulty. Ever since they drafted the specific list of attributes which they considered essential to qualify a commodity for entry into the futures markets, it has been discredited in actual practice. The list of qualifications that they set up can be found in many textbooks, to wit:

1. The commodity must be a basic one.
2. It must not be perishable.
3. Units of the good must be homogeneous and fungible.
4. It must be one for which the price fluctuates frequently and with wide amplitude.
5. It must be a product that can be accurately graded.
6. It must be measurable, both quantitatively and qualitatively either by weight or cubic content.
7. The supply must not be controlled by monopoly interest.
8. Nearly all manufactured articles, especially stylized ones, are unsuited for futures transactions.
9. A broad market should exist for the good, possibly a world market.
10. Finally, it should be a product that is salable at all times for liquidity.

These were the specifications set up by the early writers and still followed by many. Time has repudiated these strict product characteristics limiting entry to the charmed circle because they were not consistent with the needs of the market on one hand,

and in harmony with the changing technology effecting the handling and distribution of agricultural products on the other. These superficial guidelines would have excluded such items as eggs, butter, potatoes, dressed poultry, etc. and yet some of these items have been bought and sold in futures for the past 20 or 30 years or even longer.

To specify variability of price as a prerequisite is a contradiction in itself. One of the strong arguments in favor of a futures exchange is that it stabilizes prices and lessens the amplitude of price variations. Technically, no product is strictly fungible. The futures contracts usually provide for divergencies from the "basic grades" and often establish a schedule of values for each variation from the "basic grades."

Moreover, it is not necessary to deal in a product that is readily and equally salable at all times. Every product offered on exchanges involved some factors of seasonability either from the demand or the supply side, and all futures markets alternately have their periods of animation and lethargy. One can conclude from this analysis that, at least, some of the limitations portrayed by the earlier writers are more imaginary than real. Let us say, they were largely fictional based on too few observations of a technique not, then, too fully evolved. The mode of evaluating future expectations by use of executory contracts in a free market may still be considered in its primacy. The proof, in my opinion, is revealed by the fact that one commodity after another has crossed the barriers, and they are being bought and sold as futures with varying degrees of success in the principal commodity exchanges both here and abroad wherever commodity exchanges are permitted to exist.

Now it is freely admitted that "angus" are "angus" and "wheat" is "wheat" and that the two are dissimilar in many respects. This dissimilarity imposes different procedures in grading, shipping, handling, storing, and conversion to use. Let us raise this question, however. Are these dissimilarities decisive in determining their eligibility as a commodity upon which futures contracts may be based, and if so, why?

Not too long ago, it became my duty to serve on a regional research committee which aspired to study the market quality of wheat. The discourse at our first session by agronomists, bio-chemists, economists, plant pathologists and other specialists on the nature and contents of a kernel of wheat was a revelation to me. It was pointedly emphasized that one of the major problems confronting the bakers of the nation was the wide range in the quality of bread wheats. The causes for such variations have mystified the technicians for years. Apparently, some va-rieties were known to be highly desirable for the purpose while others are not so desirable. One particular variety was abso-lutely worthless as a bread wheat and yet it was grown and sold for that purpose in the same areas where high quality bread wheats were grown. A recent news item serves to emphasize the importance of producing acceptable varieties of wheat. Early in August, 1966, U.S.D.A. designated 36 varieties of wheat as unde-sirable for price support under the 1967 price support program. Moreover, such varieties (all specified in the announcement) will not be eligible for premiums and will be discounted 20 cents per bushel in the price support loan and purchase rate for 1967 crop wheat. At the same conference, it was revealed that the quality of flour obtained from any particular variety of wheat, even the better ones, erratically depends upon where it is grown, seasonal changes in climate, soil conditions, rainfall, and other factors. One could only conclude from this evidence that wheat, after all, it not just wheat. The need of the millers in buying bread wheats is more and more definitive analysis, such as bak-ing tests, laboratory research, field inspections, etc.

I relate this tale of woe about wheat production so those of you who may be plagued with the notion that deliveries of live cattle on futures contracts presents an insurmountable barrier (be-cause of inability to accurately determine grades) to the con-tinued success of such contracts may be reassured that the diffi-culties, if they do exist, are not singular or unique to the cattle trade.

Animal products (animated or otherwise) may and probably will be subjected to innumerable tests before they are accepted as a qualified medium upon which futures trading may be estab-lished. We should always be aware of exigencies that might arise to threaten the existence of any established organization however solidly it may appear to be founded.

The point I wish to underscore in this instance is that the failure of any particular futures contract does not preclude subsequent attempts to trade in the same commodity on a futures basis. The fault may lie in the imperfections of the contract, the location of the market, available financial facilities, mischievous intrusion of exogenous forces, or any number of other factors none of which may implicate the inherent characteristics of the commodity itself. It is my belief that nearly everything produced in this economy may be bought and sold in futures, since nearly everything we grow or manufacture today is already being sold under contracts ranging from "to arrive" or "deliver contracts" to futures contracts. Moreover, barring unfavorable legislation, the volume of transactions in futures will continue to rise as the population increases, and as the technique of trading in futures spreads to an ever increasing number of persons who understand and appreciate this means of facilitating and directing distribution.

The ebb and flow of futures trading may be strongly influenced in another way — by the personnel choosing this mode of doing business. The brokers, speculators, scalpers, spreaders, and others engaged in live cattle futures may be constituted differently through environment, temperment, training, and natural aptitudes than those currently engaged in the business of dealing in colonial goods, metals or grain. It takes time to create an institution, formulate the rules of conduct, develop customs, establish tradition, and attract a body of traders dedicated to serve the public and collectively perfect their own mode of organized behavior. The traders in grain futures have been in operation in this country for 99 years (1867 to 1966) — the live cattle futures less than two years. The difference in experience between these two groups could well be a major factor in the success or failure of any single venture. All we need do, is to look back on the history of the grain trade to realize that the road to success is not always free from obstructions. Competitors, meddlers, vested interests, and other intruders will be prone to place impediments along the way to retard progress.

[62]

BASIC CONCEPTS PERTINENT TO FUTURES TRADING

It was my privilege to attend the conference held here in July 1964 at which industry representatives debated the means as well as the wisdom of introducing and implementing a beef futures contract. Candidly, if anyone had been so audacious as to predict that about 46,000 contracts would exchange hands in the first year of trading, that this number would be more than doubled in the next 8 months and the total value of all the trades in the first 20 months would exceed one billion dollars, I feel sure his listeners would have voted him the Burlington Trophy for having the liveliest imagination in the year 1964. Nevertheless, this is what happened in the live beef futures market on the Chicago Mercantile Exchange in the period from November 1964 to May 1966.

In answering the question, "are dissimilarities in the commodities decisive to determining their suitability for futures transactions?", my answer is broadly an unqualified no. It is my contention that nearly everything extant in our economy is now being bought and sold either under contracts "to arrive" or "deliver" or as futures. The reason for this phenomena is that our market system resembles, in some respects, a five-ring circus. We are simultaneously engaged in transferring rights and titles in the following ways:

A. Gift giving
B. Barter
C. Purchases and sales for cash
D. Contracts "to arrive" and "deliver"
E. Futures transactions

Volumewise, the transfers under A, B, and C are relatively small in comparison to those consummated under D and E, probably because of our credit economy. In portraying this market image, it is not my objective to relegate the cash market to a role of minor importance. It is an essential institution in which forward transactions are ultimately culminated. The sum of all the transfers under A, B, and C might amount, in this economy, to 10% of the total transactions in our credit economy. Physical deliveries under futures contracts tend to be less and less the longer such contracts are in use, and the greater the volume of trade under each option. The percentage of contracts terminated by live cattle deliveries since the inception of this option was only 13/1000 of 1% at the close of the first 8 contract periods or through mid-year 1966. Western cattle deliveries were 2.15/1000 of 1% for the two contract periods.

As an economy evolves from simple to complex stages, it becomes necessary to develop a more sophisticated market system to clear the trade. In this country, market transactions are channeled primarily through three avenues. The first of these is the cash market.

This kind of market is designed to facilitate the transfer of titles to specific lots or quantities of physical goods in exchange for cash on the spot. Such a market institution is invariably strongly influenced by terrestrial conditions effecting the production and utilization of commodities. The cash markets are patronized in the main by producers, processors, and consumers who enter these markets with a clear purpose of acquisition or disposal of rights associated with particular goods which may not be fungible or duplicated in kind, degree, or quality.

The things which are bought and sold in these markets, nevertheless, are rights and titles giving ownership and control to specific units of goods. The sellers impart and the buyers receive possession of the goods immediately or shortly after the transaction. Failure to receive delivery of that which they have selected might result in a real economic loss and cause considerable inconvenience to the principals involved. The breach of such a contract should entitle the aggrieved to specific performance or adequate compensation in a court of law to obviate any economic loss which in some instances exceeds the actual value of the original goods.

The prevalence of this form of trade interlinking the transfer of rights to the physical delivery of the good creates a subjective attitude toward all transactions. This inclination to overstress the importance of corporeal goods has adversely influenced an objective analysis of contract markets.

The contract "to arrive" or "deliver" is a phase of market development that has been grossly neglected by scholars and authorities specializing in market theory. The transactions in this category represent an intermediate position between the cash and the futures markets. The deals are usually for specific units or lots of goods or their equivalent. Deliveries are called for after a lapse of time and payments may be made at the time of delivery or shortly thereafter. Agreements on the transfer of title in this case may be made on samples, but they are also commonly made on description. Remedy for breach of contracts in this classification are vested in the courts of law.

Futures contracts have been negotiated among traders ever since 1697 according to the latest research reports on their origin.[1] The primary role of a futures market is one of determining prices for the present and projecting them into the future. Such a market gives direction to the whole movement of goods and commodities into channels of use through objective contractural commitments. It interrelates values or prices at the different centers of trade.

Secondarily, in these markets, risks may be shifted from those who do not have the inclination, the capacity, or the resources to carry them to those who specialize in risk assumption. Furthermore, the net result of this form of trade provides a continuity of market opportunities that cannot be obtained in any other way. Those who enter this market do so with a clear intention of trading in rights and titles. Rarely do they ever intend to receive the physical commodity as a result of their transactions with the possible exception of those who engage in selective and anticipatory hedging. The traders of futures fully intend to make settlements by paying differences in cash rather than receiving deliveries of physical commodities. In the first place, a majority of these traders have no means of utilizing the corporeal goods if they were forced to receive them. And secondly, such physical deliveries probably would not meet specific requirements if recipients were in the packing or processing business.

This writer believes that businessmen familiar with futures contracts recognize that no one can be forced, in a squeeze, to make physical deliveries of a commodity which the seller does not possess or who finds it impossible to acquire. The courts of

---

[1] Bakken Henry H., Futures Trading Seminar Vol. III, Pages 8-16 Mimir Publishers Inc. Madison Wisconsin 1966

equity, where such cases are sometimes settled, have positively determined that the debtor may pay the difference in cash to the creditor.[2]

In pondering over this situation, I have concluded that in reality we have two separate and independent market institutions. Each is a separate and distinct entity. They are organized to perform a specialized function. In this milieu, because of scope of operation, number of participants, volume of business, and its faculty to project prices months in advance, the futures market is invariably the dominant institution. Under the circumstances, the futures markets and their corollary cash markets seek their own price plane, but they unerringly approach the maturity date of the futures contract in a horizontal parallax, though they are influenced by similar forces within any given universe. The chief motivating forces are the factors of demand and supply which may vary slightly with reference to each series of rights and titles. As a result, the two markets closely resemble one another in the values or prices they establish as they course through time.

To summarize the foregoing line of reasoning, if each market is a separate and independent entity; if each is free to move price-wise in its own sphere; if remedies against breach of contract are vested in separate courts; if each performs a series of specialized but somewhat dissimilar services; and physical delivery is an imaginary illusion that need never be real; it is a vestigial concept of an age-old custom that may be relegated to oblivion whenever the enlightened enterpriser chooses to cast it into discard.

A limited inquiry directed to brokers, traders, and market specialists was made concerning the differences and similarities of the live beef futures contract compared with other futures options. These interviewees were located in five major market centers of the mid-west. Everyone questioned, with slight reservations, was of the opinion that fundamentally no differences are apparent. A futures contract is a futures contract. The commodity traded in does not alter this fact.

---

[2] Board of Trade vs. Christie Grain and Stock Company 198, U.S. 236 (1905)

No world-stirring decision could be derived from such a limited survey of opinions, but it was evident that the experienced practioners interviewed recognize that in a futures contract one actually acquires title to an equitable right in either an intangible or incorporeal property rather than an absolute right in a corporeal good. This right is valuable because it provides contractors an opportunity to profit from the transaction, but conversely they must also assume the risks of losses from changes in the market prices of such rights. These experienced traders realize that legally it is impossible to force delivery of a corporeal good under such contracts if the other party to the agreement chooses to settle the difference in cash.

Up to this juncture, hedging has not been alluded to as a possible factor in adapting the futures contract dealing in live cattle. One could wish that more research data were available covering the whole universe of futures trading so that the nature, cause, and effect of this form of business could be analyzed with a greater degree of accuracy. Until the necessary spade work is done in digging up such factual data, we can only hypothesize on that point.

It has been proven historically, I believe, that the practice of hedging slowly develops after a futures contract becomes firmly established as a dependable option. The statistic cited, excluding Western cattle deliveries, indicates that only 13 contracts in every 10,000 transactions were terminated by the delivery of live cattle in this first period of experience. One might conclude from these figures, that some segments of the industry, or certain classes of traders are cautiously withholding action until the live cattle futures contract is rooted and reliable. Moreover, it is my opinion that those who use the futures primarily as a hedge are those who may, under certain conditions, permit contracts to terminate in physical deliveries. If this line of reasoning is tenable, the commodity exchanges involved in introducing new contracts have much at stake. If successful in their ventures, they can reasonably expect an increase in the volume of trade, and such increase is desirable because it will broaden the market and tend to further stabilize the contract.

[67]

FUTURES TRADING IN LIVESTOCK

Whatever may be said about the merits of hedging as a service, its role in futures trading is of inestimable value primarily as a means of risk transference, and secondarily, as an added source of income to the commission brokers and the exchanges. Holbrook Working has classified this phase of futures trading into several categories and has attempted to prove conclusively that a hedge is a technique that can be used to make a profit between a purchase and a sale. My position is that of a skeptic. It is my conviction that the hedger assumes a neutral position in the price determining function because essentially no risks are assumed that are not statistically counterbalanced over a period of time by subsequent hedging transactions.

If futures contracts in live beef are expertly drafted, the volume of business they will produce as hedging transactions may supplement other forms of trading up to as much as 25% of the total volume of futures transactions. With this statement of adaptation, the affirmative rests his case for the critics to assail.

Paper presented at Live Cattle Futures Study Conference-Chicago on September 8, 1966.

Do Live Cattle Futures Differ from other Existing Futures Contracts?

by
Gene A. Futrell
Iowa State University

I want to compliment Professor Bakken on his scholarly and interesting paper. He has raised several points that will provide the basis for further discussion. I note that Professor Bakken closed his paper with the words, "the affirmative rests his case for the critics to assail." I had not really considered this a debate in the formal sense with me on the negative side – since I do not consider myself "anti-livestock futures." I do feel that we can accomplish more by looking objectively at the nature and characteristics of the futures market in live slaughter cattle, and to explore the adjustments, if any, in application, market strategy and logic. These appear necessary for enlightened and effective usage in testing the new market by hedgers, and by speculative interests. Perhaps differences in viewpoint or misunderstandings can thus be resolved and clarified.

In my opinion, Professor Bakken discards the need for serious study of the live cattle futures market in his statement that a "futures contract is a futures contract" and through his obvious and expressed faith in the ability of the futures market mechanism to adapt, given sufficient time, to whatever obstacles impede its progress temporarily. But I doubt that this will be much help to the cattle feeder who is relatively unfamiliar with the futures form, and is trying to learn if the market has potential as a management tool for his business; or for the Extension educator or classroom teacher attempting to increase understanding of the market; or even for the commodity broker trying to promote the futures market to cattle feeders on its hedging merit. With due respect to all futures markets, I find it difficult to agree with

Bakken's view that they are a development of greater significance than the coinage of money, the Emancipation Proclamation, or the institution of private property rights. Certainly the record of failures and limited successes, along with numerous examples of notable success, in futures trading attest to the fact that all commodities at *particular times* are not equally adapted to successful trading in futures contracts. Whether success or failure at a particular time results from fundamental characteristics of the commodity in question, from inept specification of the contract, taxing regulations, or from temporary conditions of market environment, may be debated. The questions that I believe need discussion here are these: Do cattle, the cattle industry, and the cattle market possess characteristics (physical. institutional, or otherwise) that limit the present adaptability of cattle for futures trading in general, and for hedging in particular? And are there differences in live cattle futures which demand different information and approaches for most effective use of the market? Despite Professor Bakken's reassuring report, I'm not completely convinced that "a futures contract is a futures contract" — except in a legalistic sense. In other words, I feel there are characteristics of the cattle market that make live cattle futures different in some respects from other existing futures markets.

Later, I would like to suggest several aspects of the cattle market, and the futures market in live beef cattle which I feel warrent careful appraisal and discussion today. But first, some additional comments on certain points in Professor Bakken's paper.

I would first agree that all of the attributes often cited as necessary for successful futures trading (i.e. non-perishable, homogeneous, etc.) are not necessarily required for a successful futures market. But some of them may enhance the chances for success. And certain of them may limit progress of a market at certain times or cause failure — because of relationships to other institutional or physical characteristics of the market or commodity concerned.

Some agreement of the criteria for a successful futures market would be helpful today. What is a "successful" futures market anyway? Bakken cites eggs, butter, potatoes, and dressed poultry as commodities that have disproven the traditional guidelines for success. Many might question the degree of success achieved by some of these commodities. In my view, a successful futures market must be used for hedging or pricing roles by a significant number of buyers and sellers. I am sure this criteria may be too limiting or ambiguous. I hope there will be further comment on this point in our discussion later.

Professor Bakken brings out several other points with which I generally concur. His point that "wheat is not wheat" is a good one, and indicates that live beef cattle do not present unique problems with respect to delivery conditions. Although the ease and feasibility of delivery was one of the early concerns expressed by many people, numerous deliveries have been completed — and apparently without serious problems.

I also agree that the new markets will be subjected to many tests of its performance as it strives for full acceptance. But this is desirable, in my opinion, provided the markets are given ample opportunity to present their case. Certainly, as Professor Bakken points out, it takes time for a market and its participants to formulate rules of conduct, strategy, and expectations about market behavior.

I have a feeling that Professor Bakken's discussion of the five ways of transferring rights and titles overstates the current position of contract and futures transactions in our economy. Since neither of us apparently has the factual data to prove the exact role of these transactions, I will only agree that they are of extreme importance. Perhaps the volume of speculative trading in some futures contracts inflates the relative importance of this method of actual commerce.

My major differences with Professor Bakken's point of view are concerned with the latter portion of his paper. In discussing futures markets, he assigns as the primary role, "one of determining prices for the present, and projecting them into the future." Providing the mechanism for registering specific prices for future delivery is, of course, essential to the hedging and speculative transactions that are conducted on the futures exchange. But I don't believe the futures market has any unique ability to determine prices for the present, since the cash market price reflects an evaluation of the same known and expected market influences.

The discussion concerning the relationship between spot and futures markets seems not wholly consistent to me. Although each market is, indeed, a separate entity, I cannot concede the degree of independence suggested by Professor Bakken. Yet, after emphasizing the separate and independent nature of the markets, he states they are influenced by similar forces and comments that "The two markets closely resemble one another in the values or prices they establish as they course through time."

Nor can I agree with Bakken's view that the futures market is the dominant institution — although I must concede that his study and experience with futures markets far exceeds my own. One of the reasons cited for the position he takes is the faculty of the futures market to project prices months in advance. Although the mechanism for registering prices in future delivery months is provided as recognized before, this is not in itself a faculty for "accurate" projection of prices. Futures prices represent a discounting of current values into the future, considering known and expected market influences and risk that is removed or assumed in the process of buying or selling futures contracts. I believe few people would accept them as price projections per se, since sellers expect prices to decline or to go no higher, while buyers expect prices to rise or to go no lower.

I do not agree with Professor Bakken's suggestions that the delivery provisions are an unnecessary frill in a futures market. I hold to the traditional view that the possibility of delivery keeps the market in the world of reality. Without this juncture with reality, the two markets could indeed become separate and independent. And in the process, the futures market would shed its economic and commercial justification for existence.

I do not concur with the results of Bakken's admittedly limited inquiry concerning differences and similarities between the live beef futures market and other futures markets. I can only conclude, based on my own comparisons, that the brokers, traders, and market specialists surveyed were not overly familiar with the cattle industry and the cattle market. On the other hand, perhaps I lack familiarity with the traditional markets.

BASIC CONCEPTS PERTINENT TO FUTURES TRADING

Professor Bakken has not looked specifically at the hedging potential of the live cattle futures market at this time — something that I'm sure is of major interest to most of the group here today and which is my primary interest in the market. Although the merits of hedging with futures contracts are acknowledged in his paper, his faith in the futures market concept leaves him assured that the market will provide this potential. And he adds an additional benefit of hedging which I would surely have overlooked — "as an added source of income to the commission brokers and exchange."

This concludes my direct discussion of Professor Bakken's paper. Despite my fairly critical comments on some points where our views are different, he has provided us with an excellent starting point for further discussion of today's topic.

I would also like to briefly suggest some other possible areas of discussion. Dr. Marvin Skadberg, who is participating in this conference, and I have tried to look at the new livestock futures market in some depth with respect to their present hedging potential.[1]

We feel there has been a general tendency to transfer conventional futures market logic to the live cattle market without a careful look at the nature of the market. And we feel some adaptation, some adjustment in application and expectation of market performance, is in order. In our opinion, live cattle and the cattle market possess characteristics that are basically different from those of most commodities traded with success in futures markets in the past. While we do not feel these differences present insurmountable obstacles to futures trading in live cattle, we do believe they limit the degree to which the market can perform hedging and pricing roles and that they increase the skill and understanding needed to effectively use the markets for hedging purposes. Without going into much detail, these conditions relate to the following:

---

[1] Futrell, G.A. and J.M. Skadberg, *The Futures Market in Live Beef Cattle*, M-1021, Cooperative Extension Service, Iowa State University, January, 1966; and Skadberg, J.M. and G.A. Futrell, "An Economic Appraisal of Futures Trading in Livestock" (paper presented at the annual meeting of the American Farm Economics Assoc. August, 1966).

FUTURES TRADING IN LIVESTOCK

1. Price-Quality Relationships — Since the Choice grade encompasses a fairly wide range of quality and weight combinations, the price range for Choice steers in the cash market is typically rather wide. By contrast, the futures price represents a single point within this range. This is significant for two reasons. One is that the price relationships between the different combinations of weight and quality within the Choice grade are not constant. The other is that the cattle feeder is likely to have difficulty in accurately estimating the correlation between his cattle (when they will be ready for market) and the weight-quality combination represented by the futures price. These conditions make it difficult to closely estimate the price that is actually established by a futures contract sale.

2. Production-Utilization Pattern — Production and utilization of beef is a continuous process. And there is a great deal of flexibility in the weight and condition at which individual cattle can be marketed for slaughter. Cattle feeders and producers can respond to market conditions and prospects by marketing cattle with greater or lesser amounts of finish, after grain feeding or off grass, etc. This makes it very difficult to closely estimate month-to-month supply patterns with any degree of precision — even though total cattle numbers are fairly well known.

3. Comparability of Cash and Futures Positions — The cash and futures market positions are not comparable until the cattle in inventory achieve minimum prescribed weight and quality characteristics. Prior to that time the cash position is represented by feeder cattle in some stage of transition to the product specified by the futures contract. Thus, the cash position can be only partially hedged, since it involves hedging of a production process rather than inventory.

4. Basis — Basis, or price difference between cash and futures markets, has no consistent and significant relationship to time periods in the live cattle market. But basis resulting from locational and quality differences is very relevant. Transportation differentials can be readily determined. But basis due to quality difference between the animals hedged and the animals specified by the contract may be extremely difficult to estimate. And there is a good possibility of substantial error.

[74]

5. Hedging Incentive — The economic incentive for hedging cattle feeding operations will likely be strong only if the futures market offers a greater opportunity for returns than can reasonably be expected from an unhedged position. And hedging away the opportunity for greater profit if the cash market turns out to be higher than the hedge position may deter participation.

6. Price Stabilization Possibilities — Stabilization of market supplies and prices is one of the frequently cited attributes of the live cattle futures market. I feel this is a very tenuous claim. Is there real evidence that this has resulted in other commodity futures markets, and what is the logic for expecting it to occur in the cattle market? If, in fact, stabilization is achieved, this would appear to weaken the economic incentive for existence of the market — since the price risk to produce would be materially reduced.

As indicated before, we do not feel these conditions preclude good hedging opportunities at times. We do believe it suggests that considerable skill is needed in evaluating hedging opportunities and completing the transactions most advantageously. It's been a pleasure to participate in this conference and I hope these remarks will help stimulate further discussion.

Paper presented at Live Cattle Futures Study Conference-Chicago on September 8, 1966.

Futures Contracts for Commodities in Production Differ in Application from Those Held in Storage

by
M. Brice Kirtley
University of Illinois

Professor Bakken did an excellent job of reviewing and considering the broad areas of futures markets. Most of his comments I agree with. Certain points I would like to amplify in relation to the cattle industry. Then, there are a few points where my views are different.

I should like to direct my comments more to the nature of the cattle industry and the contribution that a futures market might make to this industry rather than to a more general discussion of futures market operations. Perhaps, this is because I feel that I have a greater understanding of the operations of the cattle industry than I do of the operations in the broad areas of futures markets.

Certainly the traditional lists for the requirements for the successful operation of a futures market are no longer applicable. Experience has indicated that many of these can be successfully overcome. The obsolescence of previous guidelines is more nearly the rule than the exception both in present day business and agriculture.

Timing is exceedingly important in any enterprise. What was not feasible and successful ten or twenty years ago may prove to be a tremendously successful venture under present day conditions. As you all know, the changes which have occurred and are occurring in agriculture and related businesses are tremendous. The great developments which have occurred in the cattle industry make this a timely period for the introduction of a futures market for live cattle. To quickly review some of these changes, the consumer market for beef has expanded tremendously. Per capita consumption has exceeded a hundred pounds annually, as compared with levels of fifty to sixty pounds twenty years ago. Beef production has more than doubled in the past twenty

[76]

years. A sizeable amount of this increase in beef production can be attributed to the great increase in grain-fed beef. Currently about 60% of our beef production is grain fed. The percentage twenty-five years ago was less than half as great. To achieve these increases in production, cattle feeding has become a specialized, volume operation. In 1964, 40% of the cattle marketed were from lots with capacity in excess of a thousand head. As you are well aware, the concentration of feeding has shifted westward. On January 1, 1956, Illinois accounted for 10.7% of the cattle on feed. By January 1, 1966, the percentage was only 6.7%. Yet, actual numbers being fed in Illinois for the two years were quite comparable. We had just expanded. With the expansion and concentration in larger operations, the need for capital in cattle feeding, as in other agricultural enterprises, has increased. The risk element also has become a much more serious factor. When a load or two of cattle were fed on a general farm of 160 acres, the investment in cattle represented a rather minor percentage of the farm business. This is no longer true with a specialized cattle operation. To fill a lot with a thousand cattle would represent roughly an investment of $150,000 for cattle alone. Moving up to 10,000 head, a not unusual size operation, the requirement would be $1.5 million. Hence, the need for greater amounts of credit is readily apparent.

With this increased volume of operation, fed cattle prices have continued to show a great amount of instability. A quick examination of the average monthly prices for Choice steers at Chicago for the past ten years will show that generally the minimum price fluctuation from the high to the low month in the year was at least $5.00. This means a variation of 20% to 25%, a sizeable element for a risk! Not only have price fluctuations been sizeable, but they have not fitted the past seasonal patterns which were more or less predictable. Currently, any particular month throughout the year might show either the high or low price. Price fluctuations primarily are a result of variation in quantities of beef coming to market at a particular time. These wide fluctuations indicate a poor job of programming by the industry in total. Partially as a result of these fluctuations in price of finished cattle, cattle feeding has been a high risk enterprise. Illinois Farm Bureau Farm Management records indicate that in three out of the past fifteen years cattle feeding operations did not pay the cost of feed.

These various items indicate a need for a system which would lessen price risk, and give access to more capital and credit. A futures market may help to provide this.

The point is well made that the level of sophistication, experience and understanding of the personnel dealing in a futures market is important. I feel it is no less important that speculators, brokers, and others of the trade understand something of the operation of the cattle industry, than for cattle feeders to understand something of the operations of a futures market. It seems to me, that this point was demonstrated at the beginning of operations in the live cattle contract. Initially only the cash prices were reflected in futures transactions with an added carrying charge which might be expected in a storable commodity. It now appears that this situation has changed and that the market is making a predictive effort.

The key role of a futures market, as has been stated, should be the determination and projection of prices. But in the case of cattle, I think the secondary purpose of providing a means of shifting price risk is extremely important in view of the capital needs in agriculture and particularly in cattle feeding. To date, the record of the live cattle futures market in achieving the major objective of projecting price has been poor. In achieving the secondary objective of providing a risk-shifting device, the record has been much better. For the first year futures prices appeared to reflect only the current cash market. About last December, the market began to project prices about the current level. The optimism was excessive for the summer level of cattle prices. But futures has been operating entirely too short a time to make an evaluation of this matter. The reaction in various phases of the cattle cycle is important.

By comparing prices at the expiration of a contract with the average cash price at the time, it appears that feeders can establish a forward price rather accurately. One of the problems of comparison here is the inexactness of livestock grades and prices even in the cash market. As Professor Broadbent has indicated in a study of Illinois hog prices, prices of comparable hogs at a given terminal market may vary widely. I am sure this is equally, if not more, applicable to the cattle market. Even with this inexactness, a feeder is not contracting to sell the cattle he is feeding. He merely wants to establish a general level of price, which I think is possible. With the rising prices in the spring of 1965, the feeder who established a price for his cattle by a futures contract failed to get the benefit of the strongly rising cash market, but the situation was reversed this year.

A futures market, to operate successfully and be an integral part of an industry, must have provisions whereby contract delivery can successfully be made. In actual practice, deliveries should be few, if any. The low number of deliveries that have been made in the live cattle contract would indicate that a good contract has been prepared. At this point, I feel that it has been successfully demonstrated that it is possible to deliver on these contracts, but it is usually not desirable.

In the actual routine operations of a futures market, I would agree that a live cattle contract is perhaps like any other commodity contract. Yet, the purpose of a contract for a commodity in production is far different than for holding inventory of a stored product. The trade should be aware of these differences. I will not attempt to comment in detail on them, but Professor T.A. Hieronymus of our department has covered this point extremely well in an article on "Futures Trading in Hogs" in the July issue of *Illinois Agricultural Economics*. Briefly, he indicates that futures trading is shifting the risk on goods in production rather than on a store inventory. Such a system would provide the opportunity for establishing a price for livestock at other than the delivery time. In writing a production futures contract, a key consideration is that a production contract must not be storable. In this way the normal market flow will not be distorted.

More research data and effort are definitely needed in the futures markets. One point among others of importance to evaluate the live cattle market is the need for information on the open interests — who is involved and in what position? Are cattle feeders in the market to shift risk, or are they on the other side as a speculator with a long position? Personally, I have known of some cases of each. Quite logically, a cattle feeder might be in the market as a speculator. He understands something of the industry from his actual feeding operations. He is familiar with the risk involved. This may be quite a proper operation as long as he understands that he is carrying rather than shifting risk. In fact, futures contracts may serve a desirable function in lessening overexpansion and excessive capital investment. Thus, the fellow who has a hundred head of cattle in the lot and decides the market looks so good that he would like to put in an additional hundred may be doing the industry a favor when he takes a long position rather than expanding his feedlot for actual feeding. At least, if he goes broke, there are less physical facilities for someone else to come in and attempt to fill. Concerning the open interest, it would also be desirable to know how much other persons with industry affiliations, such as packers, market people, etc., are involved. Logically, from a risk shifting viewpoint, only a cattle feeder should be involved. Risks at other stages in the industry, because of the short time periods and rapid turnovers, are rather minimal. Such a study of open interests would add not only understanding, but, I believe, confidence from the cattle industry.

Futures trading simply provides a cattle feeder with an additional tool in the operation of his business. He must understand the capability of this tool, when it is feasible to use it, and how to use it, or secure competent advice before he acts. A futures contract cannot remove all of the risk in cattle feeding. There will be periods when, in his opinion, the market does not reflect the future with sufficient confidence. While he may fix a price by a futures transaction, he will also limit the possibility of gains from a rising cash market. Therefore, he must decide whether his best alternative is to accept the returns which would be assured from a futures contract or to simply carry on his routine feeding operation. An important test of the futures market for cattle will be the period when the cattle cycle is in a decline. Will the speculative side of the market develop price expectations that are optimistic enough to encourage participation from cattle feeders?

[80]

There is considerable difference of opinion, as to the influence of a futures market on price stability. Possibly the effect of a futures market may be slightly different in a product in production rather than in storage. Personally, I feel a futures market may contribute to stability in cattle prices. Excess weight has been a major factor in recent price declines of slaughter animals implying that a fee is paid by hedgers to speculators in much the same way that I might buy fire insurance on my house. It further implies that hedgers decisions are neutral with respect to their impact on prices and that the decision to hedge does not involve choosing among alternative actions on the basis of price.

There is no doubt that hedging does, in fact, reduce risk, but the usefulness extends much beyond the idea of transferring risk from a beef hedger to a speculator, so my purpose today is to outline a much broader view of the role of futures prices and hedging in livestock marketing and production. In particular, I am going to try to argue or present arguments that futures markets and hedging can be viewed as operational tools that can be used as guides to decision making by marketing firms.

— — — — — — — — — — — — — — — — — — —

The following two papers were presented as commentaries to the foregoing paper at the September 8th, 1966 Study Conference on Live Cattle Futures. It might be helpful to the readers of this volume if they bear in mind, "That it is not physical commodities, but legal rights which are bought and sold in the markets of the world." This fact reduces all goods to a common denominator in their transfer from hand to hand, and the marketing function is specialized in the creation of possession utility. This concept applies to all manner of exchanges whether they occur in cash markets, in spot markets, or in futures markets.

In contrast, the production functions yield elemental, form, place, and time utilities. These are eminently useful characteristics of the corporeal good itself, and are of general concern to the millers, packers, processors, bakers, and ultimate consumers. Their appraisal of the good is based on its inherent composition such as its appearance, chemical composition, caloric content, and numerous other attributes. This array of subjective values may or may not be conducive to a monetary evalua-

tion at the time of sale because some of them are not determinable without laboratory analysis.

The commentators, in this instance, have undertaken the difficult task of attempting to show that live cattle futures differ from other traditional futures contracts by relating the trades to a subjective consideration of certain physical characteristics of the product itself which are useful, real, and necessary to sustain life. There appears, however, to be no catalyst that will permit interfusion of material matter with abstract attributes of legal rights in common terms.

The brokers and traders in the world's exchange centers and elsewhere are as often as not unconcerned, oblivious, and incurious about materiality. They are specialists in negotiating the terms of exchange in determining the kind, degree, nature, and duration of legal rights to incorporeal and intangible properties which are offered in exchange for a similar array of rights in other goods, services, and properties with the hope of making profits without sustaining losses. This is an economic service primarily dedicated to the business of determining prices in advance of the ultimate transfer of the product into the hands of the final user.

An Editorial Observation

Paper presented at Live Cattle Futures Study Conference-Chicago on September 8, 1966.

The Role of Market Prices

by
Rollo L. Ehrich
University of Wyoming

The primary function of both cash and futures prices is the coordination of economic activity. Prices are the signals that guide business decisions, including choice of product, volume of product, timing of purchases and sales, and so on. These innumerable decisions by thousands of individual firms in turn determine the prices through transfers of ownership or rights of ownership in the market place.

Economic activity can be effectively coordinated only if marketing institutions are conducive to efficient price discovery. Efficiency of pricing or price discovery refers primarily to accuracy and speed of determination, and effectiveness of the distribution of price information through all sectors of the market.

The pricing mechanism of futures markets has certain unique characteristics, compared to other types of marketing institutions, which contribute to increased pricing efficiency. Trade in a standard contract allows concentration on conditions that apply to the price *level*. This abstracts from another market function, that of evaluating certain specific lots of a commodity. Trade by open outcry in a centrally-located place increases the competitiveness of pricing, in that all trades immediately become public knowledge and individual bargaining power is reduced in importance. Professional speculators increase the numbers of competitors, and bring increased market information to bear on the formation of these prices. Another, somewhat underrated, contribution of futures markets to pricing efficiency is the highly efficient information system that usually develops along with the growth of a futures market.

These elements of efficient pricing must be qualified with respect to price accuracy. No matter how efficient the mechanism

[83]

is itself in finding prices and discovering prices, the price signal is of value in decision making only if prices are based on all possible information, and only if no technical condition or friction develops that would distort the signal. These conditions depend to a large extent on the degree to which the futures market is used by all classes of traders. Both the quantitative and qualitative character of the information that affects futures prices depends heavily on the use of these markets.

Now, price signals can be distorted if the market is technically imbalanced because of a lack of adequate speculative activity. Typically, hedging tends to be imbalanced on the short side because many people want to hedge by selling. To balance short sales requires purchases on the long side to absorb this imbalance of hedging activity. If the market is technically imbalanced, then the futures prices will be biased and, it will be less useful to business firms, as a tool for decision making.

Expected Livestock Futures Price Behavior

What types of price behavior can be generated by livestock futures markets? A futures market should generate prices, which are the best available estimates of prices expected to prevail during the respective delivery months. This is a simple concept, but it can be a best estimate only in terms of the fact that you have only a certain amount of current information available on which to form these prices. Therefore, the most that can be expected of a futures price quotation, even on the better-traded markets, is that it is unbiased and based on all possible information that is currently available. Because it is quite impossible for an individual firm to evaluate even a minor fraction of all forces that do affect prices, I think the existence of a market price which is the result of trading on a basis of all possible known information is a net addition to the decision making tools of individual firms.

Livestock futures markets are still relatively young, so little empirical evidence relating to price behavior is available. However, because these markets are relatively thinly traded, it is probable that prices generated on these markets are biased in some way and without further evidence, it is probably reasonable to expect that the price signals currently generated on these markets are of limited usefulness as price predictions alone. But, despite this shortcoming, hedging on the basis of these prices can be a reliable and useful tool in decision making, if the bias is predictable, and if one views this bias as a cost element in a hedging program.

Now, to shift gears a little bit away from futures prices, I would like to ask the question: "How do livestock futures prices relate to the cash market?" Again, in my opinion, it is too early to answer this question in solid empirical terms. We can get some indication of expected relationships by drawing on the experience of older futures markets. I am going to present some hypotheses about what we should expect in the relationship of cash to futures prices. One might expect that cash and futures prices should be equal during the delivery month, assuming that quality and location specifications for the futures contract is identical with the specifications of the particular cash articles that you are interested in. We all know that various factors will introduce inequality in most specific comparisons, including differences in delivery terms, dressing percentage, grade differences, and geographical location. So, it becomes the burden of each prospective hedger to estimate the expected delivery month relationship between the futures price, i.e., the price of the standard article traded in futures markets, and the value of a specific lot of livestock.

What does delivery month price equality mean to the prospective hedger? Briefly, it means that regardless of the relationship between cash and futures prices at the time a hedge is placed, gains (or losses) on the futures transactions will tend to offset losses (or gains) on the cash transaction, i.e., if a trade is carried into, or very near to, the delivery month. It means further, that the futures price quoted at the time a hedge is placed tends to be "locked in", that is, it tends to become the actual price received (or paid) for the livestock.

What about futures transactions, and what about hedges that are not carried into the delivery month? Can a hedger predict, within reasonable limits, the change in the relationship between cash and futures prices prior to the delivery month? Are cash prices tied to futures prices in any systematic way during time periods prior to this delivery month?

[85]

Going back to experience from other futures markets, in particular, the experience witnessed on the futures market for storable commodities, there are some things that we can say about the expected cash futures price relationship in terms of storable commodities. One of these things is the spreads between cash and futures prices, and between futures prices for different delivery months. These are recognized as a reflection of the current level of supply as it relates to the current level of demand. I want to emphasize the word *current* here, in the case of *storable commodities*. In particular, cash future price spreads for storable crops, which are produced seasonally and, therefore, need may be viewed as current *prices of storage*.[1]

Holbrook Working theorizes that the current price of storage is the major factor which affects prices in distant futures, and these tend to have equal impact on the cash prices in the market, i.e., on current prices and the prices of nearby futures. Again, according to his theory, the spread is affected only by factors relating to current supply and demand. The spread is not affected, according to his theory, by expectations of changes in supply and demand conditions.

The important fact, in terms of interpreting futures price signals and placing hedges according to these signals, is that expectations, while influencing the level of futures prices, are also reflected in current cash prices, so new information regarding future conditions will not normally change the spread between cash and futures prices. Rather, major changes in cash future spread

---

[1] For stored commodities whose production is definitely seasonal, cash future spreads may be interpreted as the current market price for the storage service. Viewed from a somewhat different angle, the price of distant futures is the market's best estimate of expected prices based on currently available information, and the spread between cash and futures prices is a direct measure of current supply and demand balance. If current supplies are large and the demand for current consumption is relatively stable for all time periods falling within a year, then competitive market behavior will force the cash future spread to be approximately equal to costs of storage. It must be recognized that the "convenience yield" associated with carrying a minimum level of stocks makes it desirable to carry some stocks at negative prices of storage (futures prices under cash prices) which negative prices would be associated with relatively small available supplies.

Working, Holbrook, "The Theory of Price and Storage", American Economic Review, December, 1949.

will be caused by changes in *current* supply and demand, referring to storable commodities. These current conditions, in my view, are much more highly predictable with greater accuracy by the hedger, than the more distant events.

Can we expect the implied cash and future price relationship for livestock to be tied together by the same economic forces that seem to tie together cash and futures prices for storable commodities? Can we expect this, even though livestock obviously are not storable?

There are alternative hypotheses with regard to cash future price spreads for livestock that we might consider briefly. The first, is that cash and futures prices are independent in the sense that futures prices reflect expected supply and demand conditions, and cash prices reflect actual current supply and demand conditions. The second hypothesis is that both cash and futures prices reflect expected conditions about equally, and that the spread between them reflects current demand relations to current supply.[2]

The second hypothesis is the hypothesis that grows out of looking at older futures markets, and looking at the behavior of cash and futures prices in storable commodities. The last hypothesis in my opinion can be rejected on logical grounds, but we do not have enough empirical evidence to really reject it. On practical grounds, finished livestock cannot be carried forward more than a few weeks at the most, because maintenance of the livestock is expensive and quality changes are going to be substantially affected as livestock is carried beyond a certain period. Thus, there is no real choice between selling or carrying forward in "storage" as in the case of grain or other non-perishables. In absence of a choice of holding, carrying forward, or selling out, current prices will be affected solely by current supply and demand. This is the hypothesis that has not been tested empirically. Permit me to expand somewhat on the theoretical reasons for this conclusion.

---

[2] Each of these hypotheses abstracts from differences in cash and futures prices that are caused by quality and locational differentials. I am assuming that cash and futures prices each reflect an identical commodity except for the element of time.

The affect of price expectations on current prices operates through the mechanism economists call, "reservation demand.[3]" Supplies that are made available for current consumption, in the case of stored commodities, depend on the price expectations of holders of that commodity. If future prices are expected to be low relative to the price currently quoted on cash markets, more of the commodity will be released as current supply causing current prices to fall. The reverse is true when prices are expected to be higher at some future date. So, both cash and futures prices are affected by expected future supply and demand conditions.

Without the possibility of significant intraseasonal storage, there is no reason to expect cash prices for finished livestock to reflect expectations regarding prices for several months in the future. Reservation demand can influence the timing of sales of finished livestock within a period of probably several weeks, but possibly not for longer periods.[4] Therefore, cash and future price spreads for livestock will tend to vary directly with the difference between *current* supply and demand conditions and *expected* supply and demand conditions. One exception would be the last few weeks of trading prior to a given delivery month. During the last weeks of trading in a particular contract, the price spread will tend to be affected, i.e., the cash futures price spread will tend to be affected primarily by current supply and demand conditions. Cash and futures prices will be tied more closely together in the last few weeks than during earlier trading months.

What do these somewhat tentative conclusions imply regarding the use of hedges in livestock futures? Briefly, let me tender the hypothesis (based on the expectation that cash and future prices will move parallel) that hedges placed and lifted during time periods remote from the delivery month will probably involve considerable risk of change in the spread between cash

---

[3] Ezekiel, Modecai, "Statistical Analysis and the Laws of Price", Quart. Jour. of Econ. Vol. 42, February 1928, pp. 199-227.

[4] It is impossible that "reservation demand" can influence the relationship between cash and futures prices for periods somewhat longer than a few weeks if slaughter of non-finished animals is a significant practice. If non-finished animals are slaughtered, then, futures will not be sold as hedges. This action will act as arbitrage between cash prices and futures prices to reflect current supply and demand conditions.

and futures prices. Hedges placed just prior to the delivery month, or carried into the delivery month, should involve less risk of these spread changes.[5]

There is a cash and futures price relationship that does behave something like the relationship outlined for storable commodities. In the case of expectations of future price levels for fed livestock, the price of feeder animals should be tied very closely to the futures price for fed animals. Expectations of future price levels for *fed* livestock should affect the price of *feeder* animals several months prior to a delivery month. The cash future spread in this case may be viewed as a market-determined price margin for feeding livestock that will be marketed at the specific future date. A rise in the future price of fed livestock should be reflected in an equal rise in current feeder animal prices, assuring a purely competitive market providing costs of feeding continue unchanged. Under competitive market conditions, livestock will be purchased for feeding if expected proceeds exceed profits from an alternative enterprise. Thus, through actions by feeders, in selling futures and purchasing feeder animals price spread will be induced thus tieing the two prices together.

Next, let us consider the hedging use of futures markets by livestock producers and livestock marketing firms. The relationship between feeder animal prices and futures prices, and the fact that futures prices tend to equal cash prices in the delivery month, combine to make futures prices in hedging a powerful decision making tool for the livestock producer. Most livestock production involves a time lag, the lapse of time between the decision to produce and actual production. Thus, the decision must be based on price expectations, that is, the decision to produce must be based on price expectations. Futures prices, we have seen, are the market's best estimate of prices expected to occur during a delivery month. This price is on the basis of current available information. Such a price is certainly an improvement over what an individual can estimate, but it still cannot be considered what the future price may be for the physical commodity at time of delivery, because new information may

---

[5] Assuming, of course, that delivery-month technical difficulties, such as squeezes, are not a significant factor.

alter the situation completely. The futures price does become a relatively fixed "expected price" from the point of view of an individual firm; if futures are sold as the production process is begun. An example of a decision to place cattle on feed is, I think, a convenient illustration of the decision making process that I have tried to outline.

In the short run, the potential cattle feeder generally has only a limited number of choices in the uses of his labor and capital. Typically, he can choose various combinations of grade, weight, sex, and age of cattle to feed. He has some scope to vary the rations used. He may also have the alternatives of selling the feed, or feeding another class of livestock. The latter alternative is probably not open to so-called "commercial" cattle feeders who have heavy prior commitments in specialized equipment and labor etc. The typical farmer-feeder, in Midwestern regions may be the exception.

It is assumed, in order to simplify the example, that the potential cattle feeder has already rejected the alternative of feeding other classes of livestock. The process of rejection could involve comparing cattle futures with hog futures. The price of hog futures and the price of cattle futures could be compared for various delivery months in order to decide whether to feed hogs or cattle, on the basis of these future price relationships. Let us assume that a particular farmer rejects hogs and decides to feed cattle because he believes that hogs are not a real alternative after all. He still has a couple other choices. He may decide to feed cattle or not to feed. If he does not go into a feeding operation, he can sell feed. Still another choice to make is what type, weight, and grade of feeder cattle to buy if cattle feeding offers adequate returns.

Now, the cattle feeder can then consider the current prices of feeder cattle, estimate his feeding costs, and if prices for the relevant future delivery month appear to offer a profitable margin, the cattle feeder can sell futures and buy feeder cattle. Sale of futures as a hedge can fix the price margin between feeder cattle and fed cattle within a relatively narrow range of possibility, because cash and futures prices tend to be about equal as the delivery month approaches, or during the delivery month. Regardless of whether price levels subsequently rise or fall, the price margin that was available at the time he placed the hedge is virtually fixed through hedging.

I would like to emphasize again that futures prices and the ability to hedge provide a mechanism for aiding these decisions and futures are not primarily a mechanism for reducing risk *after* the decision has already been made. Viewed as a decision making tool, futures prices and the ability to hedge in futures can increase the range of decisions that are feasible for a given business firm. The cattle feeder in our example could choose between several types of cattle and feeding programs with increased precision, given a structure of predicted prices for various dates in the future. For example, potential profits from long-fed steers (600 lbs. or less) versus potential profits from short-fed steers (600 - 800 lbs.) can be pinpointed by comparing current prices for the two types of feeder cattle and futures price quotations for relevant future delivery months.

Futures Prices and Marketing Decisions

Now, this is an example of hedging and the aid to production decisions. I would like to briefly outline some ideas about how marketing decisions can be aided by the use of futures markets and prices. Cattle feeders have some scope for choosing a range of time periods of sale. Cattle may be marketed any time within a several-week period. The most profitable time will depend on expected prices relative to calculated additional costs of feeding. For example, after cattle reach a choice grade, and weigh around a thousand pounds, the manager, still has a chance to increase profits by feeding to higher weights. Hedging in futures can help pinpoint expected profits or losses, thereby removing some of the uncertainty which would inhibit this action in the absence of a futures market.

Turning to meat packers, I think I will offer some hypotheses along these lines. Meat Packers' buying and selling decisions can be aided by futures prices and hedging. In particular, I think, forward contracting by meat packers could become increasingly feasible with the existence of a futures market. Detailed analysis of the potential advantages or disadvantages of forward contracting, as such, is beyond the scope of my remarks today. However,

I would assume that operational efficiencies of two types may be forthcoming from the use of forward contracts. First, forward purchases will enable individual packing firms to make more efficient use of plant capacity. Second, customers' demands for particular types and qualities of carcasses can be met more effectively by purchasing livestock on contract. The ability to hedge, thereby establishing a relatively firm selling price, enables the packer to measure the profitability of forward contracting versus operating on a hand-to-mouth basis. That is, the packer is able to make the decision on whether to go into forward contracting for delivery to his customers on the basis of futures prices and market opportunities therein.

Some scope may exist for the packer to consider entering forward selling arrangements with retailers and wholesalers on the basis of futures prices. Hedging can be used as a convenient temporary substitute for purchases of livestock to fulfill these forward commitments. As an example, suppose a retailer were to bid for delivery of beef carcasses over a two-month period in the future. This may be a far-out supposition, but just suppose for a moment that you were in a position to receive bids for delivery of livestock or carcasses over a several month period in the future. The consideration of whether or not to do so, or the feasibility of making such a forward sale from the point of view of the packer, would require a reliable estimate of the purchase price for cattle. The relevant futures price can provide this estimate. Further, if the packer decides to accept an offer for future delivery, he can still hedge this transaction by selling a nearby futures contract to fix the actual purchase price within narrow limits of possibility. He can then shop around for the desired type of livestock, simultaneously lifting the hedge as the livestock are purchased in the cash market.[6]

---

[6] An example of this type of hedge is the flour miller's "operational" hedge. Flour millers price the raw material (wheat) in estimating the profitability of a forward contract price for flour, by buying futures as a temporary substitute for later spot purchases of wheat. Because forward sales of flour are normally made for periods of less than 60 days, the miller is reasonably certain that cash and futures prices will move approximately parallel to one another. The purchase of futures, therefore, will establish the net price of wheat that is ultimately paid.

The success of either type of hedge, i.e., selling futures against forward contracts for livestock or buying futures against forward sales to retailers, will depend on the predictability of the relationship between cash and futures prices. As was shown earlier, cash prices will tend to equal futures prices during the delivery months. The net price results on contractual arrangements that terminate in or near a delivery month are reasonably predictable. However, cash-future price relations prior to delivery months are less predictable, because as detailed above, cash prices are expected to be primarily influenced by current conditions, and futures prices should be primarily influenced by expected conditions. Thus, hedges placed and lifted during months remote from a delivery month probably carry considerable risk of a basis change or a cash-futures price spread change.

There is not sufficient empirical evidence yet to form a solid basis for explaining or predicting cash versus future differentials and we cannot really rely on past evidence in storable commodities for insight into what we can expect in the way of cash and futures price relationships in livestock. So, under these circumstances, prospective hedgers are well advised to go into this with due caution and take a great deal of care to develop their own predicting devices for estimating these expected changes in prices between cash and futures quotations.

Paper presented at the Livestock and Meats Futures Study Conference-Chicago on November 30, 1966.

The feed lots

A forward look at Futures Trading in Livestock

by
Allen B. Paul
USDA — Economic Research Service

Two broad conditions underlie the rise of futures. One is the specialization that is part of economic growth, and the other is that forward trading is achieving specialization. What we will have to say about livestock and meat futures should be understood against this background.

With every enlargement of the economy, there invariably are some activities that can be further specialized. It is the familiar notion associated with Adam Smith that specialization depends on the extent of the market. But also, the extent of the market depends on specialization. That is, the accretions to the real product or real income of society (which ultimately define the size of the market) arise from gains from specialization and the gains from trade.

Now, this implies something important about reorganization of production. A continuing problem of business enterprise is to search the market for areas that are large enough to sustain the output of more highly specialized operation. And when the market comes to absorb the output of many such specialized operations, then some enterprising person will take a sub-process and put it into its own specialized operation and, hence, produce more cheaply than others can do for themselves. Thus, the principal attribute of the economic growth process is that it is unsettling.

Whenever it becomes feasible to refine production further, scale economies increase, and opportunities arise to apply technology. Entire industries may be caught up in the need to adjust in what to produce, and what to own.

Arrangements for exchange also become more sophisticated. There is a set of contractual arrangements that together can be regarded as "the financial system". This system enables production to be organized on a more efficient basis, by separating the ownership of capital from its administration in production. There is a need to mobilize the saving of many indivduals and put them at the disposal of those who want to produce. There is a need to divide enterprise and apportion the responsibility for the parts among people according to individual preferences. There is a need to facilitate the shifting of enterprise plans as conditions change. There is a need to mitigate the large variations of returns so that the firm can plan to modernize and expand. This, in brief, is the general setting into which futures trading fits.

Conceptually, organized futures trading is equivalent to other arrangements that enable capital to be mobilized for efficient production. Futures does this by separating responsibility for owning commodities from their use in production. The owner, in economic terms, is the speculative interest. He may or may not belong to a specialized class; he is anyone (including farmers, processors and college professors) whose net worth is affected directly by what happens to commodity prices. His commitment influences the flow of capital, which flow appears outwardly as an investment by hedgers in inventories, facilities, labor and so on. It is deceptive that no funds flow directly from the commodity owner into the commodity business. The flow of funds, in consequence of the speculative commitment, is indirect and often not traceable under sophisticated financial arrangements.

On the other hand, the hedger's province of enterprise (as a hedger) is to produce services. Such services achieve commodity transfers in place, form, and time. Arbitrages by merchants between foreign and domestic wool markets illustrate geographical aspects; hedge selling of potatoes by growers at planting time in the form of November contracts illustrate form aspects in turning fertilizer, seed, some land, and labor into a potato; and hedge selling of grain by terminal elevators on receipt of grain at harvest time, illustrate time aspects. Futures trading in livestock and meats merely extend these opportunities to market services in form, place or time.

So much by way of orienation. In September of 1959, William Wesson and I gave a paper at a Chicago Board of Trade Seminar. It was a dull period for futures. Price supports, state trading, vertical integration, contract farming, and attitudes reflected in the onion and potato experiences, all seemed to be against it.

[96]

BASIC CONCEPTS PERTINENT TO FUTURES TRADING

The 1958-59 year was disappointing. The average open contracts for the five major kinds of grain (including soybeans) had declined from the previous year. Some of the younger brokers wondered aloud whether it might not be wise to leave for greener pastures. We were asked to discuss the future of futures trading at a seminar. Our thoughts were put down on paper. We were optimistic — perhaps more so than some people at that time thought valid. We tried to put matters into perspective. Despite the long-run failure of futures trading as a whole to grow over three decades, there was underlying strength in the feed, animal product, and semi-perishable product components. These favorable tendencies were submerged in the overall picture by the adverse effects of cotton and wheat. (And we surmised that the latter had about reached their limits.)

Basic forces were examined. The business of producing feed crops and livestock were being separated and increasingly specialized. Less feeds were fed where grown. More were entering livestock production through purchase and sale. There was an increasing role for futures trading, or for equivalent arrangements, arising from the necessity of putting activities in the grain-feed-livestock sector (and other sectors) on a more efficient basis. Whether futures trading in particular cases would rise or fall alongside other means for organizing economic activity would depend on how the emerging conditions affected each.

Our optimism seven years ago was well-founded. Futures trading has made remarkable strides. The aggregate of futures activity (as measured by open contracts) has by 1962-64 increased about 40 percent over 1956-58 levels, despite the failure of cotton to come back. More important, some of the reasoning still appears to make sense and seems applicable to the problem before us. I want to quote selected passages from the 1959 paper because they set the stage for what we have to examine today.

The first quote is on the kaleidoscopic nature of futures trading activity.[1]

"The most easily identifiable influences in the failure of fu-

---

[1] Futures Trading Seminar — History & Development — Volume I P. 243-244, Mimir Publishers, Inc., Madison, Wisconsin, 1960.

tures trading as a whole to grow over the past thirty years are in the two export crops — wheat and cotton. The basic factors are the changing market position of the two commodities and, inter-related with this, the support of prices and increased State trading. The composition of commodities in futures trading has shifted over the years. Some that once were very active are now inactive or have disappeared just as trading in pork provisions and butter. Trading in some commodities has been attempted without much success to date, e.g. in canned vegetables, (which was tried in Philadelphia with the four major vegetables), dressed poultry, live hogs, (which is the phenomenon of the old livestock exchange here in '31) frozen eggs, cheese, apples, mill feeds, rice, and others. Trading in some commodities has grown to relative large volumes, as soybeans, soybean oil, and meal, eggs, and potatoes. The shifting composition is by and large a response to a set of forces arising out of the structural organization and the needs of individual commodity sectors."

We had not dealt with the possibilities of developing futures trading in fed cattle or bellies, but did keep our sights on under-lying forces on which such developments would be based.[2]

"The number of enterprises per farm has declined. The amount of farm inputs that are home produced rather than purchased also has declined. Together, these trends result in greater specialization in agriculture. Some of the more pronounced trends in crop and livestock production can be seen clearly while others, though pervasive, are not as apparent.

In recent years, the latent possibilities for further specialization have seized the imagination of many people. Important experiments in crop and livestock production are underway. These are being watched with great interest. - - - - - - - - - -

Specialization of production is a physical phenomenon. To obtain lower unit costs through specialization, the scale of physical operations, and therefore, the amount of capital invested in the operation usually must be increased. How does the economic system adjust to one person operating the resources which are provided by others? The answer is through loans, leases, part-

---

[2] Ibid pp. 225-26

nerships, syndicates, corporations, forward trading and so on. Because of business uncertainties the capital is financed both as enterprise investments and as money loans.[3]

It is unlikely that the corporate organization of farms would provide a solution. By and large, the corporation itself would attract little capital from outsiders other than from relatives and friends who might invest in any case. Be it a corporation, a partnership, or anything else. More likely, the outside capital will be secured by borrowing, leasing, joint account production, and by forward sales of output, irrespective of the legal form of the farm business."[4]

Then we examined contracting as a way of dividing up an enterprise, and thereby mobilizing capital. Now, we are going to get in futures trading. The revolutionary changes in the broiler industry were well underway at that time and this furnished us with a jumping off point.

"Man has invented various ways of dividing up an enterprise investment without dividing up the physical operation itself. Some are equal-share arrangements, like partnerships and corporations, in which all enterprisers are in the same boat. All gain or loss according to the profitability of the entire venture. Others are unequal-share arrangements in which the profits of the separate shares are largely independent of one another. Under "contract farming" and forward trading, an enterprise becomes subdivided into different parts and these parts are separately transferred to different parties according to individual preferences."[5]

The nature of the differences between "contract farming" and forward buying and selling may be readily illustrated. (Now in forward buying and selling, I see this as a generic term, it includes any form of buying and selling, including futures. This is just an institutional development.) If a broiler producer is treated essentially as a laborer working for a fixed fee, with little responsibility or reward for the success of the enterprise, then there is a wide gulf between contract farming and forward selling.

---

[3] Ibid Pp. 227
[4] Ibid. Pp. 226
[5] Ibid Pp. 228

Economically speaking, the farmer might as well be employed as a wage earner in a broiler factory. At the other extreme, if the grower accepts full responsibility for the rate of gain and death loss, then the difference is nominal. The broiler producing enterprise becomes subdivided into two parts just as house-building enterprises may be subdivided into two parts — as between the speculative builder and the contractor. The feed dealer (in this case the speculative interest, including an outside speculator) assumes the responsibility for having so much resources converted into so much meat at a later date. The grower assumes the responsibility for converting these resources. This is exactly the subdivision of the broiler enterprise that might be achieved through forward buying and selling, but the mechanics would differ. For example, the grower could provide all the inputs and at the same time sell his expected output for deferred delivery at a fixed price. Thus, his net return would be determined by his efficiency in turning inputs into outputs. No more capital might be needed under one scheme than under the other, and the scale of operations might be alike.

Most "contract farming" agreements fall between the extremes just described. They are flexible arrangements for dividing up an enterprise and, therefore, are readily adaptable to a wide range of economic conditions. At the same time, there has been an extension of forward buying and selling under fixed terms in both crop and livestock enterprises, as in growing cotton and feeder cattle. (These were days when the cattle were sold at a dance of the fall round-up, or sometimes by the calf driver.) This suggests a wide applicability of such enterprise sharing arrangements. The extension of either or both methods tends to be stimulated by the increased use of operating capital in modern commercial farming."[6]

These reflections seven years ago fairly well describe the situation in cattle feeding today.

The term "contract farming" should be replaced with the term "custom feeding". Specialization in production of fed cattle has required the development of new ownership, enterprise,

---

[6] Ibid pp. 228-29.

and exchange arrangements. Both customer feeding and futures trading serve these purposes. They are different types of responses to the same underlying need.

Custom feeding has grown rapidly. It now accounts for over one-third of the cattle marketed from commercial feed lots having 1,000 or more head capacity. Because such feed lots accounted for 40 percent of the fed cattle in the year 1964, about two and one-half million head were involved in custom feeding.[7] But along-side, active trading in fed cattle futures has developed in just two years, exactly two years. While no data is available on

Chart I
TRANSACTIONS ENTERED ON DECEMBER 1 FOR DELIVERY ON THE DATE SHOWN IN THE SUBSCRIPT

NATURE OF ENTERPRISE	EQUIVALENT TRANSACTIONS	
	"FUTURES"	"CUSTOM"
Ownership of fed cattle June	Buy fed cattle June	Buy feeders Dec = Buy feed Dec Buy feed lot services Dec — June
Production of feed lot services Dec — June	Buy feeders Dec Buy feed Dec Buy Labor, etc. Dec — June Sell fed cattle June	= Buy feeders Dec = Buy feed Dec = Buy labor, etc. Dec — June Sell feeders Dec = Sell feed Dec Sell feed lot services Dec — June

---

[7] Based on data shown in *Organization and Competition in the Livestock and Meat Industry*, Technical Study No. 1 National Commission on Food Marketing, June, 1966.

the cattle represented thereby, a few rough figures show its probable magnitude. About 14,000 futures contracts are now on the boards, that includes some from other exchanges, representing about 300,000 head at 1150 pound average weight. If one-half the short-interest represented feed lot hedging (the other half, spreading and speculation), and if the feed lot turn-over averaged five months, then one-third of a million cattle per year would be involved. This is a substantial quantity, although distinctly smaller than the quantity produced under custom feeding.

While in practice, some custom-feeders provide the feed and feeder animals to customers, rather than their customers going out and buying them. These items would be billed at cost or the feeding charges would be adjusted accordingly.

The economic equivalence between hedging in cattle futures and custom feeding is shown in chart I p. 101.

Soybean crushing services are marketed in the same way. Processors buy soybeans and hedge these in oil and meal futures or in forward sales. The market established an implicit price for the relevant service. This is a genuine competitive price that appears in the form of a margin between two commodity prices. In the case of soybeans, the value of a bushel of beans is subtracted from the value of the oil and meal derived therefrom, and deliverable at the end of the crushing period.[8] In the case of cattle, the value of the feeder animal plus the value of feed are subtracted from the value of the fed animal derivable therefrom and deliverable at the end of the feeding period.

The unique thing about animal feeding is that one can enter at various points in the production sequence. One could provide as much or as little feed lot services as he chose. To show this, we focus on feeding to a choice grade for December delivery. One can feed a calf for ten months beginning in February: a heavier animal for eight months beginning April; a still heavier animal for six months beginning June; and so on. With December fed cattle futures traded through 1965, one can derive the implicit market price for feed lot services undertaken for different duration, as these appeared during 1965. (Figure I)

---

[8] Allen B. Paul and William T. Wesson, "Short-Run Supply of Services — The Case of Soybean Processing," *Journal of Farm Economics.* Nov., 1966.

Figure I

Margin between value of choice steer, December delivery and value of feeder plus feed, 1965. (Omaha — Kansas City bases)

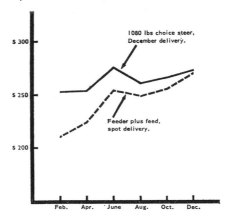

The margin narrowed as the year progressed, reflecting the fact that less services were required to bring the animal up to weight; but, the margin on any day would also have been influenced by competitive forces — the demand for feedlot services and the amount of unused feed lot capacity. In any case, the price of feeding is independent of the level of cattle prices.

The particular margins shown in Figure (1) were based on Kansas City, Omaha prices, and on fairly standard ration and weight gain assumptions. They fall in the range of 10 to 18 cents per head per day and average about 13½ cents, which is in the range of what some of these cost studies show for various size feedings — a little bit better than some of them show.

So much for the equivalence between futures trading and custom feeding. What are the relative merits?

While pricing of services is established rather directly through custom feeding, such prices are not readily known because they are arrived at through private negotiations and may involve many considerations of value. On the other hand, while pricing of feed lot services is done indirectly through hedging, the cattle and feed prices are well known and margin computations can be standardized.

[103]

For the outside speculative interest, access to custom feeding services may be somewhat difficult. Futures trading opens the gates. The hall-mark of futures is its machinery for safeguarding credit. It makes it possible to lend more against given collateral, or lend the same amount with more safety. The stranger can be fit into the scheme with relative ease.

Futures gives the feed lot operator extreme flexibility in changing his enterprise combinations. He can assume any degree of speculative position overnight. Commodity markets that are sophisticated show this behavior. In this respect, custom feeding is awkward.

Finally, futures trading fits the small man as well as the large one. Custom feeding, Willard Williams tells us, is associated mainly (and he's the one who made the study for the National Food Committee down in Texas) with feed lots having over 5,000 head capacity.[9] A limitation on use of futures by small feeders is their unfamiliarity with it. Intermediaries might arise to fill this gap. In the potato market, the fertilizer or machinery dealer does this; in the cattle market, the livestock dealer or packer might do this. At least one packer seems to think that there is business here worth going after. If you just look at it, it is not always the small farmer that would be the most likely to benefit from hedging, and futures to be a business worth going at — or he may not. It's the kind of farmer who needs capital. He may be one with a 100 head or 200, or 500 head, which is certainly not large in a general operation, and if you have, say, a $30.00 market rate of return for feed lot services above feeding cost for (X) period of time, multiply that by 200 head, you get $6,000.00 known return for 200 head feeding. If you go up to 500, you get $15,000.00, if this farmer or feeder can know he has in his return calculus for his labor, shed, machinery, gasoline; and to a fellow who is short of capital and has his eye on a piece of land somewhere, neighbor's land, wants to modernize his equipment, this may be a critical five or ten thousand dollar price of investment that he would like to lock in. He's a growing fellow, he's

---

[9] *Structure and Conduct of the Commercial Cattle Feeding Industry,* Supplement No. 1 to Technical Study No. 1, National Commission on Food Marketing, June, 1966.

a fellow who is going to be larger, so, I think, this idea of a small farmer vs. a large farmer is really not the exact way to put this matter, although there is some truth in it.

By "small", I mean the farmer who feeds 200 to 500 head annually and has profitable alternatives for capital. If hedging were to guarantee him a margin of $30.00 per head above feed and feeder cost, this would be 6,000 to 15,000 dollars. It might be the kind of income guarantee he needs from year to year to expand his overall farming operation, by adding some land, building, or major equipment.

In sum, organized futures trading appears to have inherent advantage over custom operations. But it is new and has been developing its own terrain. The Chicago-Omaha contract seems to be mostly a mid-continent contract (for hedging purposes). (Now, this does not mean that I know people out here use it just for midcontinent contracts, what I am saying is, judging from the logic of where the supply terrain is and how the prices behave on the Southwest Coast and so on, that it is largely a mid-continent contract, which is a rather large territory — all the way to the Rockies.) Custom feeding seems to be mostly a development of the Southwest, that is, the people of Omaha, Texas, and southern California. Yet, the two overlap in the Cornbelt, and they overlap to a lesser extent in the West Coast. The problem of extending the usefulness of futures over a wider area is, in a large part, the problem of finding suitable delivery terms for a market that is so diversified.

I must apologize for not examining other livestock and meat futures, but perhaps the method of thinking shown here will suggest how to approach these topics. One would search the underlying economic rationing in terms of the gains from further specializing some part of the commodity process — whether it be growing, processing, warehousing, or distribution. Then he would examine the potential contribution of futures trading toward this end, including alternative arrangements to accomplish the same thing. I would have liked to examine other futures, but this was not possible.

Paper presented at the Livestock and Meats Futures Study Conference-Chicago on November 30, 1966.

[105]

Communications — The nerve center of a market

Part III

Many Facets Govern the Evolution of a
New Futures Contract

The Factors Favoring a Futures Contract for Live Hogs Outweigh those Against it

by

Henry H. Bakken
University of Wisconsin

This Conference is being held on the eve of the first anniversary of the introduction of the Live Cattle Contract. I join with others in commending the officers and directors of the Chicago Mercantile Exchange for their courage and conviction in considering the creation of another Futures Contract dealing in live hogs imitative of the contract introduced a year ago for live beef cattle. The timing for this venture, in my opinion, is propitious. Swineland is in turmoil. It is a time of marked changes in production which often portends changes in methods of sale and distribution.

The Innovators

Much of the progress of mankind toward a better way of life must be attributed to the innovators. Not too long ago, the theorists who claimed to know something about Futures markets were saying that it would be impossible to establish a Futures contract in animate objects. They were preoccupied in listing the characteristics which would qualify the commodities suitable for trading in Futures, such as being homogeneous, fungible, nonperishable, freely available the year around, etc. Live cattle, most assuredly, was not one they had in mind. These theorists remained undaunted when eggs crashed the gates of the Futures market. They raised their eyebrows when onions and potatoes rolled under the barriers, but they have been slightly subdued since the steers soared over the top of the stockade. My hat is off to the practitioners who dare challenge these preconceived notions. There are those who will have their fingers crossed on the proposal to offer live hogs in Futures. They are the perennial pessimists who are with us always.

[109]

FUTURES TRADING IN LIVESTOCK

Trends in Production

During the past 5 years, 1959-1964, the number of hog raisers has apparently declined at the rate of 100,000 per year. It is estimated that the 1965 Census will report not more than 1.3 million hog producers in contrast to 1.8 million in 1959. In the meantime, the number of head of porkers slaughtered has been falling over 200,000 head per year on the average if farm slaughtered animals are included in the accounting. The number of hogs marketed in the United States in 1964 exceeded 85 million head valued at over $3 billion. Less hogs per producer of better quality represent the current output by fewer farmers, who are ostensibly more efficient producers. These changes on the production front have induced repercussions in the processing and distribution centers. The live hog of today is a different animal from those of the yesteryears.

The Federal standards and grading system as a consequence is antiquated and needs to be brought up to date with the advancing

Figure 2

Swine distribution U.S.A.

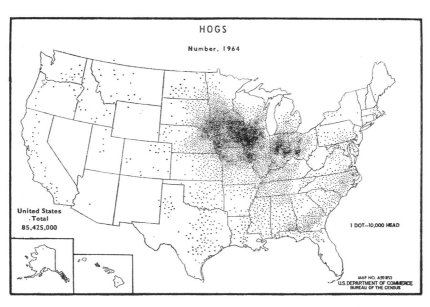

technology in production. Those who draft the provisions of the new Futures contract should be cognizant of this aberration.

Under the circumstances, not a few packers and processors have seized the opportunity to introduce their own grades and standards. These invidious standards add to confusion in the distribution system and make comparisons difficult, if not impossible, both in quality and price to ultimate consumers.

The Oligoposonic Technique

In March, 1965, there were nearly 2,200 firms engaged in slaughtering hogs in the United States, but only one-third of these were located in the 12 North Central (midwest) states in which approximately 84 percent of the hogs were produced.

The pricing system in the cash market for hogs has never been efficacious. The reasons for this situation are expressed in theoretical terms in another section of this report. In my opinion, research in the area relating to pricing techniques might reveal variations in pricing more erratic than need be. The introduction of a Futures contract in this situation might well add more stability to the market, and serve to direct production on a planned basis.

In the existing situation, the producers on the fringe experience prices for market hogs that swing in wider amplitudes than those near the center of the specialized production areas. When a paucity of supplies necessary to meet demand requirements prevails, they receive more favorable prices for their offerings than the producers near the center of the production areas. When supplies overrun current demand requirements, the producers in the fringe areas experience more unfavorable returns. Often times, they are forced to hold supplies off the market beyond the acmic point of superior quality to avoid ruinous returns.

This procedure is a common pattern in procurement by packers and processors of farm products. It results in the creation of a buyer's market. A situation made possible by the disparity between the number of producers on the one hand and the number of buyers on the other.

The introduction of a Live Hog Futures Contract adds another dimension in competition by enlarging the sphere of price-making forces. Not only does it involve more people in buying and selling this commodity, it extends market opportunities by projecting market commitments months into the future.

Limitations of the Cash Market

With the exception of one brief interlude since Colonial times, the only type of market available for live hogs here or anywhere else has been the cash market.

Prior to 700 B.C., trade was consummated primarily on a barter basis. The only alternative to this form of transferring ownership in goods or properties in ancient times was gift giving.

The cash market, even though it has been in existence for 2700 years, give or take a few centuries, has some distinct limitations that are inherent in the institution.

Some of these limitations are:

1. *Transactions are Isolated.* Many transfers of ownership are concluded without benefit of competitive bids or offers. Thus, the total market is fragmented and some of the local markets may be quite imperfect competitively.

2. *Prices Remain Unpublished.* The prices agreed upon in paired transactions are generally not publicized for the benefit of other interested parties.

3. *The Environment for False Rumors and Misinformation is Ideal.* Spurious facts concerning prices are all too prevalent; the statistical position of supply and demand is often distorted; and purported activities of rival buyers and sellers are especially noxious because they exploit the credulous to serve the ends of the unscrupulous.

4. *Prices are Erratic.* Supply and demand are rarely matched perfectly in a cash market where physical goods are transferred simultaneously at the time of the transaction. Without forward commitments and planning in production and deliveries, prices gyrate capriciously beyond points of justification.

5. *Market Raiding is Made Possible.* The medieval lawmen envoked strict censures against the practices of forestalling and engrossing. These practices still are extant in our cash markets, and just as repugnant to the guardians of Justice.

6. *The Environment for Collusive Actions is More Ideal.* Secrecy in negotiating contracts is conducive to surreptitious deals

among a few buyers and a few sellers which results in oligopolic or oligoponsic situations.

7. *Invalid Transactions are too Prevalent.* In some areas of commercial activities, the dominance of buyers or sellers (entrenched interests) have imposed their will to the extent that agreements become invalid for want of mutuality.

8. *Crude Pricing is the Rule Rather Than the Exception.* The cash market inherently has always tended to round out prices to rough approximations rather than establish values on definitive grades or classifications.

9. *Pocket Markets are Created.* Resort alone to cash transactions results in an uneconomic allocation of resources with much attendant waste. Large areas of demand remain unsatisfied and substantial supplies never reach optimal points of consumption because the market is never fully integrated through proper organizations to bring supply and demand to focal points of exchange.

While the cash market is being forced into the background in this country where contract markets dominate, it still serves as the culminating market terminating a long series of transactions preceding final delivery of goods, services, or property to the ultimate users.

Risk Transference

The modern commodity exchanges are an indispensable medium in a free industrial society. Without their facilities and services, all business would be retarded and many segments would revert to a status quo or remain semi-paralyzed. In the past, most books and pamphlets on the subject of futures trading stressed hedging as the primary service. The traders represented themselves before hostile legislators and an incensed public as respectable businessmen offering an insurance service. That is, they collectively assumed the risks of price variations for those who were either unable or unwilling to carry the risk themselves. The academicians parroted this line of reasoning going so far as to say that hedging was absolutely essential to the existence of a Futures market. I regard the function of hedging as purely incidental to the existence of a Futures market, a blessing in disguise, which adds volume in numbers of transactions, and income for those participating in a Futures market. The attribute which Futures markets have in bridging the chasm of uncertainty and providing insurance against risks is unquestionably a valuable service that is utilized and appreciated by roughly 10 to 35 percent of the buyers and sellers in a futures market.

The Art of Drafting Futures Contracts

Attempts have been made in the past to establish futures trading for various commodities with little or no success. Some contracts which have either faded out or are on their way to oblivion are the millfeeds: middlings, bran, and shorts. Others are lard, butter, cotton, and cottonseed meal.

We might for the moment ignore governmental intervention as a common cause for the demise of futures trading in some commodities.

Futures contracts fail for other reasons which focuses attention on the provisions of the document itself.

(1) If a contract is poorly drawn, it may unduly favor traders on the long or short side of the transaction. Such a contract could generate a squeeze on delivery dates, or result in some other unfair advantage that would eventually discourage buyers or sellers to participate in the trade.

(2) The concentration of market control has been cited as another cause for diminution in futures trading in certain contracts. The total supply of certain goods may be restricted in output. Producers, manufacturers, or buyers who have access to available substitutes may choose to boycott a particular futures. This is referred to as market power by economists.

(3) A few futures contracts have failed in the past because an adequate body of speculative traders could not be attracted to these options. In such instances, the market lacked liquidity and those who wished to transfer risks found the premium for such service too costly.

Futures as a Directive Force

During the past century we have evolved and developed contract trading to a higher degree than any other nation. These markets, especially the futures markets, perform a remarkable service in equating supply and demand. By virtue of their structure and form, information streams into strategic centers (the commodity exchanges) where it is collated, analyzed, and disseminated in a manner designed to maximize available economic resources. Within the sphere of these markets, men have no peers. There are no restraints other than those imposed upon themselves exclusive of the law of the land. Each according to his ability may enjoy the privilege of earning a livelihood with equal opportunity. Some of the totalitarian leaders in planned societies have discovered recently that there is no substitute for "profits", the *magic catalyst* which resolves economic problems more efficaciously than any other allurement or persuasive force.

Under the aegis of the contract markets, the factors of production may be combined in the most profitable combinations, risks are minimized, and a higher degree of specialization in production and distribution is made possible through forward pricing.

From this line of reasoning, it would seem that both providence and practicality favor action. Once again the innovators appear to be on the threshold of success.

Paper presented at A Live Hog Futures Symposium-Chicago on November 29, 1965.

A Packer's View

by
Stanley Lammers
Sioux Quality Packers

Gentlemen, this live hog futures thing has been the subject of a lot of discussion in our operation, as the establishment we have in Sioux City is strictly a hog operation. We, as a packer and as a livestock slaughterer, have for the past number of years watched this belly market. We have also watched the live cattle trade and the carcass trade; and from this I drew up a few remarks which I would like to read to you.

First of all, to make this market useful to the producer and to the slaughterer, a common denominator has to be used in delivering points throughout the marketing area which should be included in the pricing of futures; that is, based on freight differential of this common denominator.

For example, the cattle trade has two delivery points; one in Omaha, and the other in Chicago. If the producer is going to merchandise his livestock to packers, he needs this common denominator. The majority of the hogs are traded on the interior markets, and I believe that more markets would make it advantageous for the producer if they had this denominator to utilize in this market. I think it would also be advantageous for the packer if he could get a consistent amount of delivery off this market.

Many producers are accustomed to marketing their livestock in local markets and slaughtering houses. This type of market receives a large percentage of hogs that are merchandised. By using the plants and markets throughout the area, the ma-

[117]

jority of the slaughterers would be in a position to utilize the futures sold through this marketing method. This, as opposed to one or two delivering market points would be advantageous, because in marketing livestock, it is not like a frozen piece of merchandise; there are bruises, death losses, and diseases that take place with a long delivery.

Also, in running a slaughtering house, we need livestock not only ten days out of a marketing month, but we need livestock every day. I don't know what rules and regulations can be offered on this point, but I firmly feel that if a contract could be exercised every month; and follow the past performance of the futures in meat trading, it appears that the daily market and the futures market then move very close in hand.

As my good friend, Bernard Ebbing, can verify, we that purchase livestock do not always come up at the end of the day with what we set out to purchase in the morning. We might intend to buy 5,000 head of livestock in the morning, and end up by buying 4,000 or 6,000. If the futures market and the daily market would coincide to a degree, it would make it possible for the packer to buy or sell this merchandise on paper and keep an equal amount of inventory if he has over or under purchased.

Gentlemen, this is merely a theory. Whether it works or not, I don't know; I honestly don't know this much about the futures market. I'm trying to look at the things that would be advantageous for the industry today.

We find that classification and grades are two major factors in the carcass slaughtering business, and also for the people who process. Using a 1-2-3 classification, I believe the weight range should be based on 200-220 pound hogs. Another classification might include 220-240 with a discount. There should also be an allowance made for individual hogs which are not within these specified weight ranges. One will have yield factors when carcasses are slaughtered that will throw them out of this weight range. I also believe all hogs should be specified as barrows and gilts.

I feel that the grade of these hogs should represent 1's and 2's; approximately 40% 1's and the balance 2's. Hogs of this quality should be required to yield 72% hot weight and be free of pustulous diseases. If you allow number 3 hogs, there should be a specified discount for these.

The backfat thickness should run from approximately 1.5 to 1.9 on a number 1; 1.9 to 2.3 on a number 2. The length of the carcass should be about 30 inches, measuring from the forward point of the aitchbone to the forward edge of the first rib. This percentage of fat, length of the carcass and conformation are specifications which help you arrive at the primal cut percentage, which in turn makes up the majority of dollars that determine the value of a hog.

Briefly, gentlemen, these are my thoughts. They may be of some help to you people in drawing up a contract for the industry. If there is a hedging possibility, I personally think that the packers and the meat people, have an interest.

If the market is traded in only a few months of the year, there may be wide fluctuations in prices within the period that become very irrelevant to live market then. If we keep an open mind, the possibility of making this market work is evident. If the right contracts are drawn up, they could be a big asset to the producer, and to the livestock slaughterer and processor who has to buy livestock daily.

Paper presented at A Live Hog Futures Symposium-Chicago on November 29, 1965.

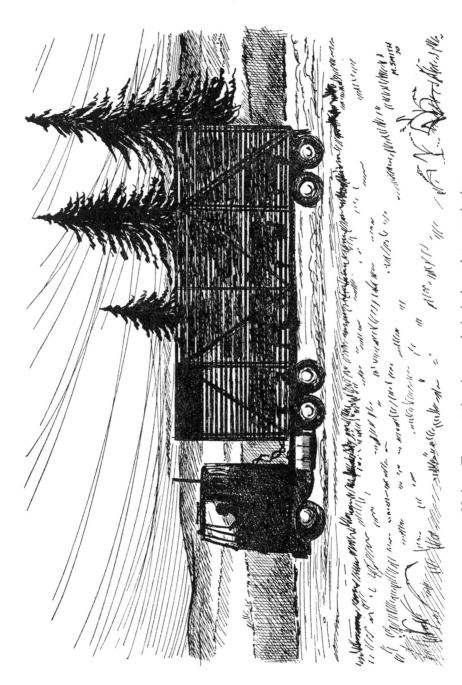

Modern Transporation has revolutionized market organization

A New Futures Contract as Appraised by a Broker

by
Glenn Andersen
Chicago Mercantile Exchange

Similar symposiums to the one we are conducting today were held by the Exchange in the case of pork bellies, hams, and live cattle. The contribution of the participants during those symposiums was invaluable. I am sure that the suggestions that are being made here, today, will be considered and encompassed in tentative specifications.

The findings in live hogs really have been encouraging. It dates back to when Henry Adlam was going around the country making a survey on pork belly specifications for the Exchange. "This is fine, but when are you going to get started on live hogs", was the question asked of him.

So it took two or three years to get the bellies going, and this year the New Commodities Committee has embarked on the live hog contract. There is just a tremendous amount of interest in it. As Mr. Lammers from Sioux City explained, he has an opportunity for forward contracting at a specific price for their use in their slaughtering program; be it a pork promotion or a cut-out promotion that includes the various cuts, it does afford this possibility, but most of all it does afford the possibility for the producer to shift the risk to the investment capital that the Mercantile Exchange is able to attract.

This is probably the only difference between the attempt in 1930 to start live hog trading at the Yard. Actually, they were trading among themselves from livestock people to producers to packers, and they didn't attract sufficient interest on the part of the investment public. It is paramount to bring in outside

[121]

capital to permit shifting risks to those specialized in this function.

We hasten to point out that live hog futures trading in no way is intended to take the place of hog marketing through your regular terminal market, and your present marketing systems. In fact, it is an additional tool that implements producer marketing programs in forward selling and forward buying.

Only two percent of the actual commodity is delivered, but it is very important to have specifications that will attract the buyer. So, as Mr. Ross pointed out, while there may be few deliveries made, we have to have a contract that the buyer won't run away from in case he is called upon to accept delivery, or in case he wants delivery.

Actual deliveries need not be effective in 48 states. As a matter of fact, this would be a great detriment to the contract because, we are not in the cash livestock business; this is the business of the packer, the producer, and the terminal marketeers. We are an agency where risks can be shifted. So the idea of terminal markets being established or delivery points being established in 48 states is not an actual necessity. The Committee is considering a few delivery points, and they will, when they are designated, afford the barometer that we need in price trends etc. that are needed. The contract is intended to provide safeguards for keeping it honest, and for making it possible for deliveries to be taken and for deliveries to be made.

The Committee will arrange to have some correlation grading of live hogs. After they are slaughtered, tests will be made for both yields and grades. This experiment will answer many of the questions that have come up today, in as far, as the final yield and grade expectancies are considered.

The recommendations, that we have secured from hog buyers, meat packers, terminal markets, and livestock interests points out that there are four factors that govern values in hogs that must be strongly emphasized. They are: average weights, uniformity, grades, and yields. So, it is important to consider the greatest volume of the quality products available. At the same time, specifications should be good enough so buyers will be willing to stand for delivery and accept delivery for their own slaughtering houses.

EVOLUTION OF A FUTURES CONTRACT

Now, Col. Lacy was one of our staunchest supporters of the 40,000 lb. contract on the West Coast because he said, "Let's give them what they want to trade — on the West Coast, they trade minimum 40,000 lb. carloads." His argument was valid and good because the Board purchased this suggestion.

There is one thing in contract specifications, as a whole, that will need to be scrutinized carefully. That is the weight size of the load. The consensus of opinion about the average size load seems to settle around 25,500 lbs. The terminal markets which the Committee will designate as delivery points should be checked to determine the most popular size of incoming loads. That is, incoming loads from the larger producers in the Mid-West, not the marginal producers. If it is 40,000 lbs., fine; if it is less that should be acceptable. It should be within reach of the larger and better quality producers in the Mid-West.

With respect to grades for delivery Number 1's and 2's seems to be the general consensus of opinion. Here again, the summations of grades will tell you a lot about what the average percentage is.

Paper presented at a conference-Chicago, November 29, 1965.

The Prospects for Trading in Live Hog Futures

by
Roger W. Gray
Stanford University

Not many years ago Everette Harris appeared to be one of the most snake bitten individuals in the world. Having foresaken his career as a university economist to become secretary of another commodity exchange nearby, he went on to become president of this much smaller struggling market for butter and eggs. A subsequent reorganization of the big market found him faced with the virtual disappearance of this market. Butter futures had long since fallen prey, as he mentioned this morning, to the Government Price Support Program. The onion futures market, which had begun to thrive here, was abolished by Federal legislation in what still stands as one of the more flagrant, if not yet far reaching abuses of the Democratic process. The refrigerated egg contract was dying the death of all markets that can no longer serve a hedging need. Everette Harris was sitting at the bottom of a deep and quiet well talking mostly to himself about such unlikely prospects as futures trading in pork bellies, and even of all things, live animals. Not many assistant professors in remote cow colleges would have traded places with him in, say, 1960. What you saw on the trading floor this morning was testimony — though hardly mute testimony — of the results of perseverance in the face of really very long odds. It may yet turn out this year, or next, that this market's center pit will be the world's largest in dollar volume. This depends largely upon soybeans or corn to come out of the doldrums on the Chicago Board of Trade. I say this not just as a personal tribute to Everette, which it is, but as a reminder that every successful futures market that I know anything about has arisen in similar circumstances of apathy, suspicion, hostility, and wide-spread misunderstanding.

Sometimes, as in the case of Kline Hall in Australia, the single-handed efforts of one person have overcome all the obstacles. More frequently, a few people have been involved, but in any case let us remind ourselves that markets do not just emerge as a free good.

Having said this, I would like to put Everette back down at the bottom of that well. I know he will get out, but it seems that the best function I can perform here today is to point out what seem to be some of the obstacles that he is going to have to overcome in developing the live hog futures contract.

Speaking in 1965 before a Futures Trading Seminar, I set forth a few general propositions under the heading, "Why Does Futures Trading Succeed or Fail?" I introduced my analysis with the disarmingly candid confession that "I don't really know why futures trading succeeds or fails." Without pretending that I have since discovered the answer to this important question, I do wish to expand somewhat upon the general argument there presented, after first summarizing it very briefly, and having earlier provided copies of that paper for participants in this study conference.

Reading from evidence of price behavior on a number of markets, it is clear that persistently biased price estimates, whereby buyers or sellers pay too much for using futures markets, provide the leading explanation for the failure of some markets to develop. The newer markets, if they are to prove viable, have always had to overcome this bias; whereas its persistence often augurs the complete demise of the market. Since hedging use is usually predominantly from the short side, downward biased price estimates, which may make hedging costs prohibitive, are commonly interpreted as reflecting insufficient competition for speculative profits.

The possible reasons for imbalance which I adduced in 1965 included contract deficiencies, market power, or simply inadequate speculation. These may, of course, be interrelated and overlapping. If hedging firms, for example, possess inordinate market power, they may influence contract terms to their own advantage, and thereby discourage speculation. Contrariwise, speculators may operate a country club market, discouraging additional competition in order to preserve monopoly profits.

While I continue to believe that the foregoing is a useful framework in which to appraise futures market performance, it will not help us very much in our present appraisal of the live hog futures market. This market has been operating for too short a period to enable statistical detection of the absence or presence of bias. Moreover, even if such imbalance could be presumed, I personally know too little about the trading composition and the contract suitability to enable me to adduce any reason for bias. Ascribing such reasons is a tenuous matter at best, requiring intimate familiarity with a particular commodity trade.

I should have wished to expand and modify the earlier framework in any event, but this is almost mandatory in the present context. In general, I incline to stress two additional factors which were only hinted at in the 1965 paper, and to reemphasize a point made in that paper which is still insufficiently appreciated, judging by the earlier live hog symposiums.

The first additional factor which I would stress may be called the institutional precursors of futures trading. If we ask a somewhat parallel question, on which I am also not expert; namely, what makes marriage succeed or fail? — We quickly appreciate the importance of institutional precursors. While the terms of the marriage contract have some importance, and the dispositions of the contracting parties have great importance, in our given environment; we should hardly expect marriage to succeed overnight in a society which had no institutional precursors. If monogamy was already practiced to a degree, and family units were already reasonably cohesive, we might expect marriage to catch on; but in a completely polygamous and polyandrous society where child rearing was a state function, marriage would probably not be an instantaneous success. Similarly, it seems to me, we need to ask what the situation was before futures trading was introduced. Some of the more important elements of hte pre-existing situation are suggested in the following questions:

(1) Was forward trading already widely practiced? There are of course many situations in which forward contracts are used which are not futures contracts. Futures trading

initially arose out of such forward trading, as a considerable refinement of the precursor. Buyers and sellers who engage in forward trading have already explicitly introduced the time dimension into their decisions, and are therefore better able to recognize the advantages of futures trading, as a safer and more convenient method of accomplishing the same thing.

(2) Is merchanting extensive; i.e., is there between producer and processor, or between processor and consumer, a well-developed business of buying and selling a commodity without essentially changing its form? This might subsist because geographical assembly and dispersion is important, or because temporal redistribution is called for. This is important because very large volumes at low unit margins place great emphasis upon price. Commodity description is usually easier because the time dimension is so apparent to one who is not affecting form utility significantly.

(3) Is there a recognizable group whose relationship to growers is such that they are likely to use futures on behalf of growers, or in furtherance of their contractual relationship with growers? Alternatively, are individual growers large enough, and sufficiently knowledgeable, that they will themselves be disposed toward futures hedging?

More institutional precursors might be mentioned but these have influenced the development of some futures market, and they may help us assess the experience and prospects of live hog trading. Before focusing upon that, however, let me mention the other additional factor which I incline to stress, after which I will be in a position to reemphasize a point made in the 1965 paper. Then I can attack what I think is a rather common *mistaken* interpretation of the live hog futures performance, and conclude by presenting two elements of what may be a correct interpretation.

The second factor has to do with the functions (the modus operandi) of speculators and hedgers in commodity futures. Holbrook Working long ago expressed his puzzlement over the observed fact that hedging in commodity futures so consistently elicited the appropriate levels of speculation. Given that the magnificent risk premiums sometimes postulated as the mechanism whereby this facilitation occurs simply do not show up in the statistics, he was long unable (and I was longer unable) to provide a clue as to the causal nexus between hedging and speculation. One conclusion which is abundantly supported in *all* the evidence, however, is that futures markets are hedging markets. So clear had this become by 1960 that Working wrote an article entitled, "Speculation On Hedging Markets," deliberately abandoning the less descriptive term "futures markets" for the case in which he sought to quantify the hedging-speculation relationship.

Not until last year, however, when both Working and I presented generalized interpretations drawn from two different approaches to two different commodities, was direct evidence provided which will require revision of some notions about the relationship between, and the characteristics of, speculation and hedging. It would strain both you and me far too much if I were to attempt to summarize that evidence,[1] but it is not amiss to briefly summarize the conclusions to which it points.

A highly successful long time career speculator once described his approach to me in the following words: "I try to find out what the hedgers are going to do, and do it first — if I tried to forecast prices I'd be dead." I appreciated neither the import nor the generality of the statement at the time, but in retrospect it is a pretty concise statement of what Working and I are saying (much less concisely). Anyone who gives it a moment's thought will realize that the temporal re-allocation of resources which is supposed to be the major benefit of speculation is actually *performed* by hedgers in this institutional arrangement. Speculators are variously viewed as: (1) providing the price forecasts (or determining the prices) which make it possible for hedgers to adjust inventories appropriately, (2) assum-

---

[1] Roger W. Gray, "Price Effects of a Lack of Speculation," and Holbrook Working, "Tests of a Theory Concerning Floor Trading on Commodity Exchanges," *Proceedings of a Symposium on Price Effects of Speculation in Organized Commodity Markets, Food Research Institute Studies,* Stanford University, Vol. VII, Supplement, 1967.

ing the risk of price change, thereby enabling hedgers to tend to other business, or (3) providing market liquidity (or simply making a market). As a matter of emphasis, rather than categorical disagreement, it is probably much more accurate to say: (1) futures prices are determined primarily by hedging, hence such "forecasts" as are implied in futures prices are the "forecasts" of hedging firms (2) most professional speculators (floor traders) accept this fact and try to profit by anticipating hedging use — whether minute-to-minute, day-to-day, or week to week (3) the avocational speculator, and the commission firm which serves him, may undertake price forecasting, albeit probably with less success and less influence than that practiced by hedgers.

This leads me to stress once again a statement in the 1965 paper, "The first prerequisite to the success of futures markets is hedging use." I doubt very much whether the framers of the live hog contract took seriously the admonitions of Professor Bakken and Colonel Lacy regarding the relative importance of hedging and speculation, stated at the earlier symposium relating to live hogs. Professor Bakken said, "the academicians parroted this line of reasoning going so far as to say that hedging was absolutely essential to the existence of a futures market. I regard the function of hedging as purely incidental to the existence of a futures market." The pejorative "academician" (like the pejorative "theorist" which appears elsewhere in his paper) strikes me as a curious way to dismiss conclusions based upon evidence,[1] while stating conclusions unsupported by evidence. I do not believe in any event that the contract was written for the public, nor do I believe that the relatively slow growth in live hog futures trading can owe to any factor other than a dearth of hedging use. Not even the refrigerated egg futures market, which came closer to it than any other, could continue to flourish without hedging use; and I'm sure the directors here were fully aware of that fact.

Beyond this, there are only two suggested explanations for the slow growth of the market (which I am careful not to call "failure"). In terms of the institutional precursors, the live hog contract may have been introduced prematurely. Neither forward contracting nor merchanting were prevalent, so a good deal had to depend upon the changing size of the feeder operation, and more particularly upon its changing organization. In both these respects, cattle feeding was much more advanced and more adaptable to futures trading. This suggests that the live hog contract could yet attract greater usage as the hog-feeding and related enterprises change.[2]

Less optimistically, it seems to me that another factor inhibiting the growth of live hog futures is the fact that you have a thriving pork belly market. Hog and pork belly values are highly correlated, and anyone who now wishes to find a reflection of hog values in futures can have a pretty good one in a very active market. It is my impression that a successful flour futures market was never established because wheat and flour prices correlate closely. A highly developed wheat futures market already existed. Moreover, it is my impression that barley futures died out because corn futures afforded a close enough hedge at a lesser cost. Wool tops futures in New York have been waning as greasy wool trading increases, etc., you don't need the one — at least not that much — when you have the other. The only situations in which a commodity has been successfully traded in futures at successive processing stages are (1) soybeans and products (where the separate product values don't correlate highly (2) cotton and cottonseed products (again, lack of correlation in prices) and (3) greasy wool in some markets and wool tops in widely distant markets (not in the same location). I do not wish to sound discouraging on the feeder cattle contract, or on any other prospects for futures markets, but must we not admit that futures trading tended to concentrate in one market at one place, and that markets for products with high correlated values be redundant.

While on the subject of this relationship, however, I ought also to acknowledge that the pork belly market experienced slow early growth. It was only after substantial revision in contract

[2] See especially, Holbrook Working, "Whose Markets?—Evidence of Some Aspects of Futures Trading." *The Journal of Marketing*, Vol. XIX, No. 1, July 1954 and Roger W. Gray, "The Importance of Hedging in Futures Trading; and the Effectiveness of Futures Trading for Hedging," in *Futures Trading Seminar: History and Development*, Vol. I, ed. by H. H. Bakken et al. (Madison, Wisconsin, 1960).

terms, as brought out in the study by Mark Powers[3] that the pork belly market grew spectacularly.

As an afterthought, I might better qualify a statement that was made earlier about hog feeders having to become larger before they would be in a position, or be disposed, to make better use of futures markets. The important point for futures market growth is that the firms be large, not too large though, because at the other extreme one of the precursors, or one of the conditioning factors which helped the development of livestock and livestock products trading on this Exchange, was a movement in the other direction, de-concentration in the meat packing industry.

Finally, events on this market, of all places, ought to teach me not to be a Cassandra. Those of us who believe better marketing is desirable (that should include all of us) ought to seize whatever opportunities we have to study this market in far greater depth than I have and to make more constructive suggestions than mine have been.

---

[3] Powers, Mark J. "Effects of Contract Provisions on the Success of a Futures Contract," *Journal of Farm Economics,* Vol. 49, No. 4, November 1967.

Paper presented at the Live Hog Futures Study Conference-Chicago on November 16, 1967.

Characteristic Variances of Live Animal Futures Contracts

by
Gene A. Futrell
Iowa State University

Being a discussant at a conference such as this is easiest when the main paper presented contains a number of ideas or viewpoints with which the discussant disagrees. Then one can simply play the critic's role and take issue with the other person's views. In the process, it is often possible to get by without offering any constructive commentary of your own. Professor Gray's paper doesn't permit this easy way out. I think it is an excellent paper. I feel it is a realistic discussion of some of the things that seem to influence the relative success of futures markets. And it raises some points that should stimulate further discussion and contribute to better understanding of the live hog futures market.

Since I can find little in the paper to be critical of, and since it would be redundant to simply express accord with what he has already said — there's only one other alternative (actually there's two, since I could stop at this point so that we could proceed with the discussion). This is what I will attempt to do. Perhaps I can also find a few points on which to disagree.

I want to first express agreement with Gray's view that hedging use is a necessity for continued success of a futures market. This is the economic basis for their existence, in my opinion, and is the connecting link with reality, and to the counterpart cash market. Gray has pointed out that hedging use of futures markets has usually somehow been accompanied by "appropriate levels of speculation." I'll take his word on this point, since I haven't studied futures markets in the depth he has. However, I think it is still likely that speculative participation is influenced by other factors than hedging use of the market.

Regarding hedging, I've had some feelings that the hedging potential of the new livestock futures markets has been given a great deal of lip service by many brokers and others who have not bothered to become well enough acquainted with the hog or cattle feeding businesses to provide sound hedging counsel, or to know how and when the market can be effectively used for this purpose. I think this situation is changing as more brokers gain familiarity with the market.

Most of my remaining comments will concern three general areas — all of which have been at least referred to by Professor Gray. These are the cost to the hedgers of using live hog futures, the economic need for hedging hog feeding operation, and the live hog contract itself.

It seems to me that Gray's discussion of biased price estimates, whereby buyers or sellers pay too much for using futures markets, is quite relevant to the live hog futures market. For some reason, the cost of hedging or the premium for price protection through live hog futures appears to have been relatively high so far in the market's short history. Ken Egertson, at the University of Minnesota, has tried to estimate the cost of hedging with live hog futures in the following way. He assumed that a producer farrowed pigs each month from March, 1966, through January, 1967 — and subsequently marketed slaughter hogs each month from September, 1966, through July, 1967. The futures market, adjusted for brokerage and interest costs, was high enough throughout this period to cover both estimated variable and total costs of production — if pigs had been hedged by the sale of futures contracts at farrowing time. However, the returns over total costs for the period studied would have averaged $1.22 per cwt. higher, based on Egertson's analysis, in an unhedged position compared with a hedged position. Thus, the cost of removing the price risk by hedging would have been about $1.22 per cwt. In only three of the eleven periods included in this comparison did the hedged position yield a higher return over costs. And one of these was by the small margin of 1 cent. This analysis did not reflect any selective use of the market, but rather a fixed pattern of hedging. This is not to say that effective hedges could not have been made at other times for hogs on hand. In fact, there have been several periods when selective hedging would have yielded a higher return. There is some evidence that the premium for removing price risk through live hog futures has been relatively high much of the time thus far.

This may or may not account for the relatively light trading activity in live hog futures. I feel other factors have probably been more important. One is that relatively few hog producers have become well enough acquainted with the market to make effective use of it. Another relates to economic motivation for hedging, and to the hog contract requirements.

The degree to which hog producers feel a need for removing price uncertainty under the present size and organization of most hog operations may have limited hedging use. Although hog operations are becoming larger and more specialized, relatively small hog operations still account for a big share of U.S. hog production. For example, in Iowa in 1966, 65 percent of the farms that raised spring pigs farrowed 20 sows or less and accounted for 40 percent of the pigs raised. Only 3½ percent farrowed 50 sows or more — and accounted for 13 percent of the pigs. In addition, hogs have historically been a fairly consistent profit maker for farmers in the cornbelt, even though prices have varied considerably. The investment in facilities, breeding stock (or feeder pigs) is relatively small in most cases, compared with cattle feeding for example. Finally, feed — which still makes up a large portion of variable costs — has been largely produced on the same farm as the hogs and has not required a direct cash outlay. An indication of the relative stability and level of returns from hogs is provided by estimates of returns per $100 of feed fed to hogs, compared with other livestock enterprises. Iowa data for the years 1960-66 shows an average of $170 income per $100 worth of feed fed to hogs. The range for the seven years was from $138 to $203. Comparable estimates for cattle feeding operations show an average income of $126 per $100 of feed fed and range of $92 to $156. This is not in itself an adequate indication of net profit, since it does not reflect other costs. But per unit investment in cattle feeding facilities, for example, would be larger than for hogs; and the non-feed variable costs would be at least as important.

Under these investments and profit conditions, most hog producers have been in a relatively good position to carry the market price risk. So the incentive for removing price risk may have been fairly weak up to this point. Individual hog producers are likely to follow an unhedged route — unless the cost for price protection is quite low or there are obviously favorable hedging opportunities present. In this sense, I think the economic need for hedging is probably more limited at this time in the case of hogs than it is in cattle feeding. A possible additional retardant to hedging use of the market so far is that hog prices have been relatively favorable during the period that hog futures has been in existence.

Gray has suggested that hedging use of the market may increase as hog operations change in size and organization. This appears quite plausible. The number of larger, commercial hog operations has been increasing, and further growth is expected. Hog finishing operations organized on a large scale, specialized basis probably have greater incentive for hedging. The year's profits are tied closely to the outcome of this single enterprise. More of the production costs are likely to be of the direct, out-of-pocket variety that are hard to absorb, offset, or conceal in other phases of the farm business.

I would like to turn now to a couple of comments on the live hog contract. It may be that the trading unit of 20,000 pounds of liveweight hog is too large to fit the hedging needs of the majority of hog producers. I do not know whether this is a real limitation or not. Producers, in the 500 head or so per year and down category, might often be in the position of not having sufficient hogs of reasonable uniformity to make effective hedging use of the market.

Present differentials between alternate delivery and the par delivery point in Chicago may not be completely satisfactory. These delivery points are Omaha, East St. Louis, Sioux City, Kansas City, and St. Paul, all at 75 cents per cwt. below Chicago. A fixed transportation differential between these markets and Chicago may not be realistic. Actual differentials may be more or less than this. Differentials are not constant from day to day,

[136]

or week to week.

I think delivery at specified times throughout the delivery month rather than after the close of trading on the contract should also be given consideration.

Two characteristics of live hog or live cattle futures markets that are different from most other markets in which there have been futures trading should be mentioned. These do not necessarily limit the success of the markets; but they do influence the kind of market behavior you should expect, and possibly the *degree* of price protection available through hedging.

One difference is that the new livestock futures markets provide primarily the opportunity to hedge a production process rather than inventory of product. This can also be done with crops, but grain futures have not been widely used in this way. This does, in my opinion, limit the degree of price protection obtainable by hedging — due to the greater possibility of quality departures from the contract specifications. The relatively wide price range that is typical of the cash market for live hogs adds another limitation on the precision of hedging protection.

A second characteristic is that there can be a high degree of independence between contracts for various delivery months. In grain, contracts within a given marketing year are closely and logically tied together. Thus, something that temporarily affects the demand, for example, can logically influence all contracts — since it affects the supply-demand balance for the remainder of the marketing year. The situation in the live hog or live cattle futures market is quite different. Large market supplies or unusual demand conditions in a particular period may have no relevance to later market conditions.

Now some final observations relating to some of the other points raised by Professor Gray. I think his discussion of the influence of previously established futures markets in similar commodities (or the same commodity at a different Exchange) warrants discussion. I think this can be a definite handicap to a new contract. In the case of pork bellies and hogs, however, I don't feel the market for pork bellies is correlated closely and consistently enough to live hog values throughout the year to make this fact in itself a limitation on hedging use. Speculator interest could be affected when background knowledge of market fundamentals and trading strategy have already been acquired for the existing market.

In discussing some of the institutional forerunners of futures trading that may influence success or failure, Gray mentions the presence or absence of a "recognizable group whose relationship to growers is such that they are likely to use futures on behalf of growers, or in furtherance of their contractual relationship with growers." The presence of this relationship presumably is a positive factor in the prospects for successful futures trading. It appears that the live hog futures market meets this condition to some extent in the person of meat packers. Thus, packers can potentially use the market to hedge hogs contracted for future delivery or possibly as long hedgers to forward price some of their live hog needs. The other two conditions he mentioned (relative to forward trading and to merchanting) have not been present in live hogs.

This raises a question in my mind about the possible impact of the presence or absence of long hedging interests. Professor Gray mentioned the possibility of a downward price bias due to predominantly short hedging. Would active long hedging in a market such as live hogs offset this influence? What is the potential for long hedging by processors? A limitation for packer long hedging may be the lack of active futures market in pork products other than bellies.

Paper presented at the Live Hog Futures Study Conference-Chicago on November 16, 1967.

Some Hypotheses on the Success or Failure of Futures Contracts

by
Robert E. Schneidau
Purdue University

Taking Professor Gray's lead, and at the risk of being redundant, I would like to state my position with respect to why futures trading succeeds or fails by the following illustration. A student once taking his oral exam for his Master's degree was asked by his Major Professor, "What do you think current hog prices are?" The student being quick of mind answered by throwing the question back to the Major Professor, "What do you think?" The Major Professor astounded by this tatic stated: "I don't think — I know!" The student then responded, "I don't think I know either!" I am also in the position of the student, but even so I would like to advance some hypotheses and comments which I feel generally augment and supplement some of the points raised by Professor Gray's paper.

But first I would like to acknowledge that I found the paper interesting, though provoking, and well hedged. Certainly contract deficiencies, imbalance in market power, inadequate speculation, etc., can all have profound effects on the viability of a given commodity futures market. These characteristics determine attractiveness of the market to its potential customers.

An effective argument for the role of hedging is given. I would prefer however, to wait and see the empirical evidence to which Roger eludes before commenting on this issue. Let it suffice to say that hedging use certainly appears an important factor in the success of a commodity futures market.

I do, as a fundamentalist, however, find it somewhat difficult to believe the belly market could serve as a substitute for live hog futures. This is not to say that it cannot be done. It certainly would not appear optimal. The price relationships among bellies, other cuts, and by-products making up the value of hogs would not appear sufficiently stable to encourage high volume hedging of live hogs.

I would like to make some additional comments on the likely success of live hog futures and the changes it might help precipitate. Since farmers are the likely hedgers in commodity futures, most of my comments will be with this group in mind. You will recognize that many of these comments have been discussed or alluded to in Gray's paper.

The introduction of both cattle and hog futures trading was certainly a milestone for commodity futures. Many thought cattle futures would never get off the ground for they violated, to considerable degree, the long established criteria for successful futures trading. Among these were: inability to easily and adequately standardize, and the inability to store the commodity over a significant length of time. Yet, enough people felt there was sufficient economic grounds for the market; that these traditional limitations were not as severe as anticipated, and that they could be overcome. After getting off to a slow start, cattle futures have become a viable market. At this point most antagonists have re-evaluated the strength of the traditional factors for successful trading, and for the most part will agree that cattle futures do, on the whole, meet the necessary criteria as now conceived. In my mind, trading in live hog futures possesses similar "limitations". It is partially for this reason I am enthusiastic about this market.

I believe trading in live hog futures by various segments of the swine industry may significantly effect hog marketing in the next several years. The possibility of reducing market risks and expanding capital availability is open to farmers.

Contractual arrangements may increase, and packers may operate more efficiently. Just as the development of faster gaining meat-type hogs has had a significant impact on pork production, the development of the futures market as a marketing tool is likely to have a significant impact on the way we price and market hogs.

[140]

Currently, however, trading actively in live hog futures is limited. Some believe that trading is too inactive to provide the fluidity the market needs for quick and equitable transactions. Partially because of this, and partially because of the biological and the economic nature of the commodity, there is and will undoubtedly continue to be a much greater proportion of selective rather than routine hedging such as exists in grain. What, then, will determine the potential use of live hog futures either directly by farmers or indirectly through packer hedgers. Two conditions are prominent:[1]

1) *The importance of the commodity or enterprise relative to the total business.* Since hogs are a major enterprise in the cornbelt, this condition is met.

2) *The amount of price risk the operator is willing to bear.* Increasing specialization and increased debt of farmers lead to increasing interests in methods useful in reducing risks.

Successful farm operators depend, to a large extent, upon volume rather than market speculation to secure adequate returns. Larger, more specialized units are particularly vulnerable to market price fluctuations. As volume increases, capital requirements increase and debt rises. Much borrowed capital is generally in use. These operators who continually utilize their facilities to the maximum may be quite willing to forego chances of windfall profits from changing market conditions in order to protect returns arising from production. The fact that these changes are taking place should lead to greater use of live hog futures. To the extent that they are not far enough along would help explain the slow start of the live hog futures contracts.

In addition to the opportunity for hedging, a viable hog futures market offers several other effects.

Farmers may find that capital is more readily available; that bankers and other lending agencies are more willing to loan money on hedged commodities. This may make possible greater expansion of operations since borrowing capacity has been in-

---

[1] The above assumes "traditional criteria" for successful trading are met and that contract mechanics and equitability have been worked out. Implicitly assumed is sufficient price instability in the basic commodity market.

creased. It also encourages operations on even narrower margins than in the past.

The existence of a viable live hog futures market could provide some degree of price stability to the feeder pig market by placing a floor under feeder pig prices, provided sufficient producers have the alternative of feeding pigs to market weights at a profit. The existence of futures contracts for slaughter hogs provides the feeder pig producer with definite information as to the relative profitability of selling feeders or fattening hogs protected by hedging. If the spread between the current price of feeder pigs and slaughter hog futures becomes too great, the alternative of feeding will result in the removal of some feeder pigs from the market, thereby causing prices to rise. When the spread narrows, more pigs will be moved as feeders. These actions could place an effective "lower limit" on feeder pig prices.

That an active futures market will result in increased price stability in the live hog market is open to question. Insofar as operations may be planned on the basis of futures prices, and that producers may react by increasing and decreasing production to anticipated, rather than current or past price levels, increased cyclical market price stability may result. Contractual arrangements in hog production and marketing may be spurred by the development on contracts made possible by futures trading. The possibility of packers contracting with farmers for prices agreed upon well in advance of delivery of the live animals is a reality with the implementation of futures trading in live hogs. Currently, one large national packer offers farmers the opportunity to contract their hogs for a price agreed upon prior to delivery. An Indiana packer offers farmers contracts which specify price, weight, grade, and time of delivery, as much as four months in advance of marketing. The rate of such contractual developments will be an important factor in the growth of the live hog market since even though farmers can deal directly on the futures market for purposes of hedging, many will not, preferring to contract, thus, letting the contractor perform the necessary hedging operations. This has long been true in grain.

In summary, it appears the stage is set for continued growth and development of the live hog futures market, and that it will likely have the effect of stabilizing hedgers' incomes, at least to the extent that hedging represents protection against declining incomes; that it may serve to encourage increased production; and that it will likely provide for more efficient orderly marketing. Whether this will materialize in the short run is open to question.

Paper presented at the Live Hog Futures Study Conference-Chicago on November 16, 1967.

Part IV

Experiences in the Practical Use of Futures
Contracts in the Marketing of Livestock

An International Grand Champion-Modern

Financing Live Beef Cattle Futures Contracts

by
Walter W. Minger
Bank of America

For the year ending September, 1965, livestock feeders in California placed 2,319,000 cattle on feed. During the same period there were 2,282,000 cattle sold out of feed lots. If we assume an average market value of about $200 per head, sales out of feed lots during this 12 month period generated about $455 million.

Our feed lots have continued, particularly in the last few years, to feed about 1,000,000 head of cattle at all times. Gross sales of slaughter cattle should approximate sales made during 1965. Our feed lots have continued to decline in numbers, but increase in capacity. As of October 1, 1966, we had remaining 531 feed lots with capacity of 1,905,000 head of cattle, that is, an average capacity of 3,600 which isn't too meaningful. On the above date, there were 1,094,000 animals on feed. We usually see our feed lots stocked with 850,000-1,200,000 head or 50-65% of capacity. Based on these figures, it is a reasonable conclusion that livestock feeding in California is both a substantial business in dollars and numbers of animals involved, and is a business that is operating the year round on a fairly high level of capacity, which is probably not the case in some of the other cattle feeding areas.

Of further interest to people is that California is about 50% deficient in producing the livestock needed for our consumer market. She is also 50% deficient in producing the feedstuffs for our great cattle, dairy, and poultry enterprises.

The Bank of America has had a long involvement with California's agriculture. In the last five years, for example, branches have annually loaned somewhere between $250-$400 thousand to borrowing customers who are in the cattle business, that is, our total loans made throughout the year to range outfits, stocker cattle operators, and feeders. I think this year we will wind up with something around or short of three million dollars. These fluctuations in loans are mostly accounted for by price levels and numbers of cattle on feed.

Because of all these things, we enthusiastically endorse the idea of price insurance as it is evolved by producers' through live cattle future contracts. Because of our historic leadership in financing agricultural production in the state, because of the scale of the magnitude of this feed lot industry in our state, and because Californians eat more beef per capita than the people of any other state in the nation, production is subject to seasonal fluctuations causing scarcity and abundance of supplies of livestock and livestock feedstuffs. Consequently, on January 11, 1966, just a few months after active trading began in West Coast live cattle futures contracts, we issued a policy letter, and abbreviated instructions to all our agricultural branches on the subject of "Live Cattle Futures Contracts."

I would like to tell you the basis on which we finance live cattle futures contracts. First, we have an understanding that we will meet all the initial margin requirements, and all the margin calls that our livestock producer might run into. We do not place the hedges. We do not get into the mechanics of hedging. We want our livestock customer to select his own broker, they have this relationship, then they go into the commodity markets to do their trading. We supply the money.

The requirements are briefly these: We deal with known customers who finance their livestock operations through us. Our producers go voluntarily into the market to hedge their position but not to speculate; that they be on top of the futures market in addition to being a livestock operator, either a feeder or a cattleman; that they be experienced cattlemen, and by this we mean someone who has had good experience, not bad experience; that they have some provision for feeding out their cattle, whether they be stockyard cattle at the moment, or whether they be in a feed lot; that they are willing to assign their interests in the hedging accounts which they have with their brokers. The brokers must agree to supply us with certain reports to keep us informed about what is going on in that account.

Now, the reports we ask the broker to give us are these: we want a confirmation of the initial orders to brokers on what our client has instructed them to sell in March, April, etc. We want monthly settlement reports when contracts are closed in order to determine how our producers came out. This is required because we hold notes, and we want proceeds to pay off our loans.

We have another document that is called a security agreement, an assignment of hedging accounts, which have been approved by our legal department. This is an assignment that is acknowledged by the broker. It simply tells us that brokers are aware we have an interest in the proceeds which build up in this margin account, hopefully, that is.

We in the bank have been making loans on storable commodities for many years, utilizing warehouse receipts and other like instruments. However, as bankers, we are frank to admit that we are literally babes in the woods when it comes to dealing with futures contracts in the commodity markets. While we have our share of speculators and hedgers on the West Coast, our bank has never been called upon before to finance non-professionals, located throughout California, in their ventures into the commodity markets.

When trading in live cattle futures contracts began late in 1964, many of us were quite excited about the possibilities this new tool offered the livestock industry. We encouraged all of our major livestock feeder borrowers to sell a few contracts, so as to gain some experience in handling this new weapon. Unfortunately, as Ken Monfort and others have touched on, several things combined to make these initial ventures less successful than was originally hoped. Our feeders, cattlemen, bankers, small packers, and even some broker representatives were a long way from being intimately familiar with the whole process of getting into this kind of market. There was poor advice, inadequate timing, incomplete counseling, and certainly, indecisive action. Concurrently, with all these things, you would think this would be enough to happen to an individual; but the West Coast cash market and the Chicago futures market didn't move sympathetically. When the time came to close out these positions, and you remember that we were indecisive, there was a loss on both the futures and the cash market. These experiences were financially disastrous to some people. These experiences added to the clamor that arose for a West Coast delivery point. Late in 1965 we got a Western contract and a western delivery point which called for delivery in Artesia, California, which is near Los Angeles. In the year that has gone by, there has been a marked decline in trading in the Western Contract. Many of our livestock people are back trading in Chicago, in spite of their poor experiences of a year and one-half ago. At the same time, all of them are hopeful, for an improved Western Contract.

It is apparent that a campaign must be mounted that strikes at several fronts if futures trading in live beef cattle is going to contribute anything substantial to the livestock industry on the West Coast. We need an improved contract. We need to educate cattlemen. We need to educate the bankers a great deal more if they are going to be of real assistance to their customers. More advertising is needed to tell about the advantages, and to overcome the inherent suspicion that is always lurking whenever someone apparently offers a "free lunch."

What has been our experiences to date? Frankly, far poorer than we had hoped. Our branches were canvassed the first two weeks in October. They were financing only about 250 contracts on the basis outlined in our policy letter. Additionally, other credit-worthy customers who have sold some 225-250 contracts were financed in other ways. Hence, on the 15th of October there was probably no more than $400,000.00 outstanding in the form of commercial and secured loans made for the purpose of meeting margin requirements. Since our lending policy was put into effect, I estimate that we have lent somewhat less than one million dollars to livestock people to meet their needs for margin requirements.

In the face of such poor trade usage, what is the Bank of America's opinion about live cattle futures? Since I am also representing the Agricultural Committee of the California Bankers Association, I am speaking for all the major California bankers which are interested and active in agricultural banking.

EXPERIENCE IN THE PRACTICAL USE

We are basically in favor of programs that would tend to stabilize a business such as cattle feeding which up to now has been a speculative business, and which would provide some future price insurance for sellers of livestock inventories. We will continue to review and endorse those programs which (1) are acceptable to the principals in the commodity involved, and (2) which offer some opportunity for banks to legally extend their services to livestock customers in a mutually helpful and profitable manner.

In the last several weeks the exchange has been offered many suggestions to improve the marketability of the Western Contract. It is our conviction that the existing contract should be changed to reflect the desires of the trade. Without the strong support of livestock feeders and packers, your Western Contract performs no function. An industry generating sales of 500 million dollars would seem to have great potential for methods which would aid the marketing process, and reduce the risks from price fluctuations. You can count on us to do our part, but first, the livestock people, whose livelihood depends on their decisions, must be enthusiastic about the contribution that futures contracts can make to their business.

Since the study conference held on November 30, 1966, at which Minger's paper was given, the Western Cattle Futures Contract has been discontinued. The reason for its discontinuance was explained by Mr. Harris—President of the Exchange, in the following statement: "As the market matured it was apparent to all that one central market, heavily traded and fluid, would best serve the industry. Modern communication facilities have made it possible and desirable for all hedgers to use one market with sufficient speculation to make it liquid at all times, so hedgers may have easy, instant and economic entry and egress. Studies of correlations between various U.S. regions indicate it is feasible to hedge cattle produced in any area. On July 7, 1970, the Board of Governors of the Chicago Mercantile Exchange voted to add Guymon, Oklahoma as a delivery point for live cattle futures contracts, and Peoria, Illinois was designated as a delivery facility when new futures contracts are listed. Beginning with the February 1971 futures contract for live hogs, Peoria, will also serve as a par delivery point. The selection of Guymon, Oklahoma was dictated by an increase in the production of feed grain in the Southwest, especially in the Texas-Oklahoma panhandle where about 25 per cent of the nation's fed cattle were finished within a 150 mile radius of Guymon. Peoria was selected to facilitate deliveries from the States of Illinois, Indiana and Eastern Iowa. Effective with August 1971 cattle contract, the governing body of the Chicago Mercantile Exchange voted to eliminate Kansas City, Missouri, as a delivery point because of the infrequency of futures contract deliveries made there. Omaha, Nebraska was decided upon as the new par delivery point effective with the August 1971 contract in the event that the Chicago stockyards might be closed for cattle as it was for hogs.

Paper presented at the Livestock and Meats Futures Study Conference-Chicago on November 30, 1966.

A Packer Considers a Long Term Approach to Futures Contracts

by
A. R. Parsons
Fischer Packing Company

Today, we have been told of the development of futures trading in livestock and meat, and hedging has been explained to us. My attempt will be to discuss *how a packer can make use of futures* and this may not necessarily be how our company uses this market. Another member of the panel has described short term inventory hedging benefits, therefore, I will *briefly talk about long-term approaches to the futures contract.*

In the meat processing industry, we are concerned chiefly with beef and pork, therefore, cattle and hogs. When we look at the volume of contracts being traded on the exchange, we find there are not enough live hog contracts being bought and sold to exert appreciable influence on the hog kills of the processing plants throughout the country. However, a major packer has recently initiated a contracting program for live hogs that is being hedged in the futures market. It is believed that this program will benefit both the producer and the processor by eliminating the uncertainty of price risk to the producer, preserve the producer's independence of action, and provide him with another method of marketing. If the program is successful, it will enable the processor to operate more efficiently because he will be assured a supply of hogs. Speculation is eliminated in this program by transferring market risks from producers and processors to others who elect to carry the risk. By doing this, the processor will neither profit nor lose if prices of live hogs rise or decline. This procedure will result in a more consistant supply of hogs. Improved efficiencies will be evident which should offer opportunities for profit to the pork processors.

FUTURES TRADING IN LIVESTOCK

As stated earlier, the volume of live hog contracts traded in the futures market at this time is hardly enough to support this program for one average processing plant, let alone the pork processing industry, yet the volume of live cattle contracts is beginning to offer the beef industry the opportunities outlined.

When we study the beginning of the futures market, we learn that hedging was not used in the early beginning, but was initiated only after twenty years of futures trading. When we look to the live cattle futures contract, we find all phases of the industry are offered something that can become a highly effective tool of management, and will provide useful economic insights into market positions of the future. Live cattle contracts, or any futures contract, represent management aids to our industry only if we understand what makes up a contract, how a contract is executed, how a contract may be used, and how to evaluate the associated risks. When a cow is bred or a feeder is purchased for the feed lot, neither the rancher nor the cattle feeder is guaranteed a sale price. The same is true in the processing business when you buy cattle with reference to the beef carcass, so, therefore, by the nature of our business we are all speculators. If we compare a live cattle futures contract to cattle feeding as an investment one must conclude that in terms of risk there is no difference.

In an attempt to adapt live cattle feeding or contract feeding to the processing industry, we are immediately reminded that both Government and public sentiment may not favor packer cattle feeding. If packers, however, are to achieve the goals in beef processing that were outlined earlier in the hog contract, they must feed or contract and have fed, a reasonable percentage of their processing capacity or sales commitment. This can and is being done by operating feed lots or buying feeder cattle and guaranteeing a feed lot operator a price at slaughter with or without hedging these animals on a futures market. In this case, a hedging program would be the same for a cattle feeder as it would be for a beef processor, depending on where the profit would be assigned. If a feeder, the profit would be in the feed lots. If a processor, in the beef box. For example, if one buys feeder steers weighing an average of 700 lbs. at $26.00/cwt.

[154]

($182.00 per animal) puts on 350 lbs. gain on each, the value is increased to $276.50 per head. This results in a necessary selling price of $26.33/cwt. at slaughter.

If cattle go on feed December 1, 1966, they will be ready for slaughter in approximately 140 days or during the month of April. By selling April contracts for $27.83, which you may or may not be able to do in the near future, a profit of $1.50/cwt. delivered, can be assured or $15.75/head for the feed lot or the beef operation, depending on ownership or where profit would be assigned. The risk has been transferred, and certainly a well informed lending establishment would look favorable toward financing such an operation. The market rise or decline at time of settlement of the futures contract will give a profit or loss to the holder of the futures contract. The seller of the contract will have "locked in" a profit regardless of market conditions prior to settlement in April or at an earlier date if he decides to lift his hedge.

The futures market offers the processing industry another opportunity, especially, if beef packers or their officers were to be prevented by law, from cattle feeding. From a long term investment, a futures contract can be envisioned as a load of cattle. The investor has acquired the right to 25 cattle for a $300.00 margin plus a $20.00 commission. He need hire no labor, buy no feed, own no land, amortize no equipment, pay no vet bills, have no death losses, wade in no mud, repair no equipment, have no frozen water lines, etc. You can remain in your comfortable office and operate your present business if you are astutely aware of market conditions and as mentioned earlier, invest in the futures market on a long term basis. This can be done by maintaining a knowledge of cattle population by seasons present, and in the future, the basic economy of the consuming public, and the competitive influences from other meats. We can determine our beef requirements at a processing plant for a given month or months in the future, what per cent we want to put on feed now and for use in the months ahead. With this information we try to fill our orders. The cattle feeders, follow much the same pattern. They anticipate a market price for cattle at time of slaughter before putting cattle on feed. When there is prospect of profit they buy feeders. If the reverse obtains they sell feeders, and not feed. This same approach can be used in the period following the month the cattle are required in the beef operation to give some latitude to the paper cattle feeding program.

This could work as follows, when a cattle population decrease is predicted, then the operator should approach the market from the long side. In a period of abundant supply of cattle, the operator should approach the market from the short side. In either case, if properly evaluated, the results could be the same. In months when there are doubtful results, do not enter the market. An example of this action may be: In the month under consideration the predicted value of live choice steers is $29.00/cwt. and the futures market quoted price is $27.65/cwt. resulting in a margin of $1.35 less .08 commission or a net margin of $1.27/cwt. which is $317.50 for each contract of 25,000 lbs. This is the same as $13.34 for one 1,050 lb. live steer.

Paper presented at the Livestock and Meats Futures Study Conference-Chicago on November 30, 1966.

Some Observations Concerning
Livestock Futures Markets

by
Roy V. Edwards,
President, Wilson & Co., Inc.

I am pleased to have this opportunity to visit with you for a little while about livestock futures in general and hog futures in particular. I especially appreciate this chance to commend the Chicago Mercantile Exchange for its prime contribution during the last few years by virtue of the leadership demonstrated in establishing and promoting its livestock futures markets. Not only did the Exchange accurately identify a growing need that was evolving out of our livestock economy, but it also had the ability and perseverance to implement a program — to actually establish futures markets that have proven to be workable. As all business managers know, it is relatively easy to talk about various potentially desirable developments, but causing them to happen is the really big job.

It is my desire to spend a few minutes on three rather closely related areas. First, I think it appropriate to dwell briefly upon some of the fundamental changes that served at least in part to support the premise that the time had arrived for livestock futures markets to serve a meaningful role in our livestock marketing structure. Secondly, we wish to offer a few comments about the trading volume on these markets, and finally, venture a few observations concerning future directions.

We run little risk of overstatement by saying that American agriculture is truly undergoing a revolution, one that is primarily technological, and one that is serving to re-shape both its economic structure as well as social values. As Don Paarlberg of Purdue has so clearly pointed out in recent talks, agriculture is

[157]

rapidly losing its uniqueness. It is becoming more like other businesses, more like industry generally. Perhaps longer than anyone else, farmers have been production oriented. But now, on every hand, we can see evidences that agriculture is rapidly entering the mainstream; along with other business groups, it is becoming market-oriented and increasingly aware of the benefits of meeting the needs of its customers. This is a change in attitude that parallels business success in other fields, namely, there is no economic reason to produce a product unless you have profitable markets.

Let me underscore the word *profit*. The farmer is no longer pursuing his vocation as a way of life, but rather as a businessman — he has, and is, becoming truly profit-oriented. While it may put me ahead of my story, I will point out here, at least parenthetically, that forward contracting is one of the quickest devices available to any agricultural producer to build a predetermined profit margin into his operation — to give real meaning to profit and market orientation.

Another key characteristic of this agricultural revolution currently underway is large scale specialization. As farm wage rates keep climbing in sympathy with urban wage scales, farmers are increasingly motivated to become more mechanized and automated, to substitute capital for labor. With the upsurge of all forms of technology, past concepts of optimal size of operations have been scaled radically upward. Specialization has already come a long way in the fed-cattle industry, with over 40% of fed-cattle marketings coming out of feed lots with a capacity of 1,000 head or more. This percentage, from a 1964 survey made by the National Commission on Food Marketing, is surely larger today. A cattle feed lot with 1,000 head capacity requires a total capital investment of over one-half million dollars and there are literally hundreds of lots that are substantially larger in size and that tie up several millions of dollars in capital in each such operation. Even the traditional small farmer-feeder of Iowa, Minnesota, and the eastern Corn Belt is in process of either expanding or thinking hard about alternative enterprises—whether this be a cash-grain operation, specialized hog production, or urban employment.

Turning for a moment to trends in hog production, we learned from the recently published U.S. Census of Agriculture that the number of farms from which hogs were sold in 1964 showed a reduction of about one-third from the level of 1959. But since the total number of hogs marketed showed an increase, the number of hogs sold per farm went up sharply. This rapid trend toward specialization in the hog enterprise is expected to continue, and since I have at hand a couple of projections from Purdue on Indiana trends, I will read them to you: The number of farms reporting the sale of hogs dropped from 80,000 in 1954 to 48,000 in 1964, and is projected to a level of only 25,000 by 1974. Concerning the number of hogs sold per farm in Indiana, we have an increase from 66 as of 1954, to 156 head by 1964, and this number is projected to double—to a level of 320 head—by 1974. These numbers tell us, I think, at least two things: Specialization is taking place quite rapidly, but it has by no means acquired the dimensions of the cattle industry in terms of capital requirements for a typical commercial operation. Depending on the exact size to be compared, I think we can say that capital investment for hog operations may run only about one-fifth those of a cattle feeding enterprise.

Granted, the number of farms selling more than 1,000 hogs per farm is growing at an extremely rapid clip—for instance, in Iowa and Illinois, these farms have tripled in number in only the past five years. Farms with this degree of specialization accounted for about 10 per cent of the total number of hogs produced as of 1964, and it is surely larger in 1967.

With this growth toward larger operating units and more specialization, it is apparent that enterprise diversification can no longer be relied upon, as in the past, as a means of spreading price risk. Yet, at the very time that this form of price insurance is disappearing, the need for reduction of risk is being sharply increased. In short, the higher the total investment in an operation, and the less equity that the management has in the business, the less risk the firm can afford to bear. Put another way, the greater the odds that a year of bad losses will eliminate or greatly reduce the activities of a firm, the more important it becomes to shift those risks that can be so transferred to another party.

While oversimplified, the demand to shift livestock price risk in the years ahead may be closely correlated with the rate of growth in specialization and capital requirements.

In passing, we might take note of the fact that, unlike the red meat industry and its establishment of futures markets, the broiler business moved toward full-scale integration as a risk reducing device for the broiler grower. The latter, in this form of organization, shifted his price risk to the hatchery or feed dealer or processor by means of contractual arrangements. In appraising the features of integration, the broiler industry has been learning that it is not a price risk-reducing device—at least not as late as 1967. In fact, several segments of this industry are apparently now strongly advocating the establishment of a broiler futures market, and understandably so.

Turning now more directly to our Livestock futures markets as they have operated during their relatively short history, we, of course, know that trading volume in hog futures has been extremely modest, relative to the highly successful cattle contract. Perhaps one of the key reasons, as touched upon in my background remarks, is the fact that specialization and commercialization have not advanced nearly as far at present in the hog industry as in the cattle business. I think there was considerable awareness of this difference when the contracts were first established, and hence the cattle futures market was expected to fare somewhat better. Perhaps, we were not fully prepared for as much difference in trading volume between cattle and hogs as has materialized, and this has naturally brought some disappointment.

However, I am among those who believe that we can and ultimately will have a successful hog contract, and all that we basically need to achieve this goal are two things: a degree of patience, and some further education appropriate to the individuals and groups involved with this contract. By way of reasons for this viewpoint, I would first of all stress this factor: The combined forces of more specialization, more forward contracting, and much larger capital investments in the hog production enterprise are now rapidly underway, but they have really gotten only a good start in relation to where we may ultimately be headed.

Therefore, the passage of time alone seems certain to bring with it a growing need for the valuable service that can be provided by a viable hog futures market. At those times when we may get especially impatient with the lack of action in hog futures in the months ahead, I suggest that we remind ourselves of how patience paid off in the case of the pork belly contract. As you know, this futures market was established in early 1961, and then proceeded to limp along for over three years with a trading volume that was even less than what we have experienced in the hog futures market. I am not suggesting that hog futures will take off like a rocket, as did the pork belly market, although stranger things have happened. More likely, the growth will be gradual, depending in part upon the effectiveness of our own educational efforts.

Concerning this all-important matter of education, we know that several individuals and groups have worked hard during the past 1-½ years in attempting to bring about an adequate understanding of hedging operations among hog producers. The task has been difficult, not only because the potential hedging audience includes so many relatively small and dispersed producers, but because all aspects of a successful hedging program are more complex in nature than we sometimes realize. It is perfectly understandable that a hog producer should want to understand exactly how he is going to come out if he were to initiate or authorize a hedging operation. This is often difficult to explain in one quick lesson, even for a good teacher and an apt pupil.

By comparison, the educational task involved with our Wilson contracting program was much easier, even though it was geared directly to the futures market. Very briefly, we have been offering producers a specific dollars-and-cents price for cattle and hogs to be delivered in a given future period at any one of our packing plants. This price is based upon the futures option nearest the expected delivery date and, once an agreement with the producer is signed, Wilson immediately sells an appropriate number of contracts in that option. Contracts are bought back, of course, when the livestock is delivered for slaughter.

Now, with this type of contract between producer and packer, it is not at all essential for producers to understand hedging principles and procedures. They are, of course, often interested in the factors determining futures prices, and also our price differentials between Chicago and our plants, and our buyers do their best to explain these matters as clearly as possible.

Over the past year, our country hog buying staff has personally discussed our contract and its futures market involvement with hundreds of producers and, as you would guess, it has been both a gratifying and a somewhat frustrating experience. To give one brief example of each, we have been most pleased to confirm what we always though was true, namely, that the overwhelming majority of producers will voluntarily honor their signed contracts for future delivery, even when the price turns out to be lower than the cash market at time of delivery. By and large, these men viewed their forward pricing operation as a means of "locking-in" a predetermined profit on their planned production; they had looked at our offering price for the finished product, and then determined that their operation was sufficiently efficient to assure a satisfactory profit; they then made their price commitment and, from that point forward, the vagaries of the cash market were of no concern to them—they were too busy concentrating their energies on achieving maximum efficiency in production. This is where they had talent to apply, and this is where they had control of their environment. In short, these particular hog producers were operating like businessmen.

As to another type of experience—which you will recognize as an area calling for further educational effort—numerous hog producers have looked at the schedule of futures prices throughout the past year, and were confident that such prices were too low —that the ultimate cash market was bound to be higher. While there are several implications here, I especially want to dwell for a moment on the pricing function, and how we might establish somewhat better understanding and confidence in the country concerning futures prices.

First of all, the producer must have a clear picture of the basic responsibilities of the long side of the market, and the economic role of the professional speculators. It needs to be made more clear that this latter group is the prime influencing factor in establishing futures price levels, that their degree of business success is dependent upon their ability to accurately forecast prices, and that competition among competent speculators will automatically direct prices toward those levels that are expected to prevail as a result of supply and demand conditions in any given future period.

Secondly, and this is crucial, confidence among producers in this process will be accelerated when they know that well trained professional analysts are continually at work in providing a basis for the speculators' trading actions. Conversely, when producers hear stories of how doctors, dentists and other laymen enter and buy orders with no apparent professional analytical guidance, questions arise concerning the scientific soundness of futures price levels—and understandably so.

In a slightly different vein, I agree with those observers who believe that our new livestock futures markets do tend to place greater responsibility than ever on speculators, since the future level of livestock production can be importantly affected by them. Unlike annual crops such as wheat and soy beans, where the harvested acreage may be little influenced by the level of futures prices, it seems entirely possible and probable that prices in the more distant futures options for livestock will substantially affect the volume of livestock production, especially when these markets grow to further size and stature. But this is as it should be— soundly functioning futures markets can be trusted to guide production, and I believe they will contribute to a greater degree of price stability than would otherwise exist.

To take a simplified illustration, the professional market analyst is going to be motivated to purchase futures contracts in the cattle market when he observes that the current rate of placing cattle on feed is very low, and that the future rate of production will not be enough to satisfy consumer demand at the prevailing market. This will tend to drive the futures prices higher, and as they reach a point where it is profitable for the producer to produce the livestock, he then has an opportunity to simultaneously sell futures contracts and begin the production process. Now as these hedges are placed, the price of the futures will tend to decline and this is as it should be; a build-up in futures sales is telling the professional analyst that more production is on the way, and the futures price is his means of signaling the producer that a change in supply and demand conditions, in the delivery month in question, is taking place.

However, let us note that if the producer should be motivated by a relatively favorable futures price to go ahead and increase his production, but does so without hedging, then his actions are not immediately known and registered in the futures market, and the ultimate cash price will likely tend to be lower than the futures price. In this situation, the futures markets can hardly perform their function as a director of the flow and level of production with maximum effectiveness. Unfortunately, I fear there is no easy solution to this kind of misuse of the futures market, but it would certainly help if we had more frequent, reliable industry statistics on livestock production changes. For instance, if weekly placements in commercial cattle feedlots were available—rather than those for the past quarter or even last month, production adjustments could be made that are not now made, due to lack of knowledge.

The point that I wish to make is that the growth of a large and valuable livestock futures market places critical responsibilities upon the professional speculator that he cannot ignore. He must be a professional price analyst in every sense of the word, applying not merely art but every scientific and statistical tool that modern management has to offer. He must become not only skilled in appraising the future movements of variables that are associated with livestock prices, but he must then also, of course, be able to measure the net effects of these forces and arrive at forecasts that have a high degree of accuracy. While you may feel that I place more stress than necessary upon this analytical function, especially since the analyst is already heavily motivated to do a good job simply in the interests of staying alive, it should also be clear that our entire industry has something at stake here by virtue of the fact that futures prices can influence the industry's future volume, and this is a responsibility that cannot be taken lightly.

The year, 1968, promises to be both an interesting and challenging year for our livestock futures markets. While I can speak freely for only one company, I know that Wilson is going to work just as hard or harder in 1968 on our hog contracting program than in the past year. I am also confident that numerous other strong and active supporters of the hog futures market during the past year will continue to do so. With all of us working effectively together toward a common goal, the year ahead is bound to be an encouraging one for our live hog futures market in terms of most any standard of performance that we want to see.

Paper presented at Live Hog Futures Study Conference, Chicago on November 16, 1967.

A Cattle Feeder Views Futures

by
Kenneth Monfort
Greeley, Colorado

First of all, about two and one-half years ago I attended another meeting of this group where I very eloquently told you that live cattle futures would not work, that you should concentrate on beef futures. I trust that your knowledge of the trading volume has proven how erroneous my judgement was at that time.

The next part of my case in establishing myself as an expert and, therefore, worthy to talk to you took place shortly after the opening of trading in live cattle. After careful and complete analysis by me, I decided that I, personally, would buy some futures. I, therefore, became part of the lifeblood of the free enterprise system — a speculator.

As often happens with speculators, the market went against me. However, it did not worry me since, after all, I was an expert and had studied the specifications for delivery very closely. I came to the startling conclusion that I could, indeed, get myself out of the mess I was in by taking delivery, and having the cattle custom killed. This part of the story is history. The cattle did not yield or grade anywhere near what they were suppose to have, so I did not do very well economically. I mentioned this to several people associated with the exchange, and everyone I ran into said, "there was one way to recuperate this loss." I decided to sell some cattle. In this way, I would let someone else take delivery of the cattle when I sold them. The time came for this to happen, and the market went against me. So, I called an order buyer in Chicago, and I suggested that he should buy me some cattle to deliver on this sale I had made. I had it figured out that they should cost me about 25¢ per pound. He said that they would cost me well over 26¢. I was in the process of telling him how ridiculous he was when he said, let me tell you what happened. Last month some nut took delivery on some cattle, and he raised so much hell that he succeeded in completely revamping the whole thing. I never had the nerve to tell him, I was the nut that had raised hell. Therefore, whether I am qualified to speak here or not, I think the Exchange owed me the privilege to express myself. Now, let me talk about hedging and how it affects the cattle futures.

The cattle feeding business has historically been a high risk business. Many of us have tried in the past, and will try in the future, to minimize their risks by buying and selling on a consistent basis. In this way they will try to get the average of the market and afford themselves some protection from the violent swings of the market. There are many risks in the cattle business! Besides the tremendous price gambles and fluctuations, the feeder is faced with risks on feed costs, sickness, death losses, adverse weather conditions, tight money, etc. Recently, we have learned of new problems, hide quotas, consumer boycotts, and consumer resistance to buying high priced cuts. In short, the cattle feeding business has enough risk inherent in it even without our price risks to be a natural for a hedging operation. If we, as feeders, can pass on some of our risks to the professional risk assumers, the speculator, it makes good sense. Now, just what is the potential of hedging in the cattle business?

If we count only cattle in the feed lots of this nation, we see a potential of some eight million head of cattle. This translates into a potential of 320,000 contracts. This means that at this time only 1½% of the potential is currently hedged, if we assume that all of the sales are hedge sales. In other words, the potential of this market has barely been tapped. The potential is there. This potential is limited only by the ability of the feeder, the willingness of the feeder to use this market, and by the availability of risk money from speculators.

Let us now look at the decisions the feeder must make before determining that he should or should not hedge his cattle. Let us look at it in the light of the current market situation. Consider Greeley, Colorado, as the site of a mythical feed lot. A feeder must decide what it will cost him to feed cattle. Current-ly, a 700 lb. steer will cost a feeder in Greeley, Colorado, around 26¢ per pound delivered to his feedlot. This figures out at $182.00 per head. Four hundred pounds of grain will cost rough-ly $100.00. Death loss and interest will amount to another $10.00, making a total cost for an animal at market time of $292.00.

The steer should be ready for market in April. The current April option, (Nov. 30, 1966) is quoted at around $27.40 de-livered to Chicago. The feeder must figure a price relationship between Chicago and his own market. It would be silly for us in Greeley, Colorado, to figure how much it would cost to market steers in Chicago, since we never ship them there. We use as a basis, the historical average difference between the Chicago and the Greeley market during the month of April. We come up with a figure of $1.25 under Chicago. Therefore, our price, based on a $27.40 futures price, will be $26.15 in Greeley. Assume on a 1100 pound steer, we arrive at a figure of $288.00 which is $4.00 under our estimated cost on that steer. This is without adding the cost of our hedging operation.

Ten days ago, we had a considerably lower cost on our feeder steer and the hedge could be put on profitably. Maybe tomorrow this will again be possible. The feeder is faced with a day to day decision. He not only makes this decision when he buys his feeder cattle, but actually he must make such decision every day that he owns cattle. It is conceivable, for instance, that the cattle that we could profitably hedge today, could profitably be hedged three months from now, after they are through their feeding period.

In short, hedging provides a tool for the feeder who wishes to minimize his market risk, and assure profitability. It can be a workable and usable tool if the feeder is able and willing to figure his costs and relate these costs to the market on a day to day basis. What are the problems involved in hedging for the producer?

One of the apparent and acute problems involved in hedging is the additional amounts of money required. Cattle feeders have historically extended their borrowings to the maximum. Often times, their credit is based to a large extent on amounts borrowed, rather than on the risk. When this is the case, the feeder must decide whether that extra investment in margin for a hedging operation is justified. I realize, of course, that you might suggest that since the risk is lower, the banks should be more willing to loan additional funds. I couldn't agree more. I can give you a rather lengthy list of bankers who wouldn't agree with me. It is only fair to note that banks involved in significant cattle feeding lines of credit are as of now, not really familiar with the normal hedging operations, particularly, with hedging operations in the cattle business. These banks have for the most part done a remarkable job of financing cattlemen. It is the biggest growth industry in all Agriculture. I honestly believe that time will change the attitude of bankers with respect to hedging. Perhaps, in fact, a loosening of the current tight money situation would do this rapidly. It is hard to tell just how the banks would react if a surplus of loanable funds were made readily available.

Permit me to raise another point that I am sure you will hear more of this afternoon. This is the contracting of fat cattle by packers. The packers then hedge this commitment. Our packing plant in Greeley is currently involved in this type of operation to a rather limited degree. This has several advantages for the cattle feeder.

Firstly, he no longer must look at the day to day variations of the market. Secondly, he does not have to assume the risk on the differential between the Chicago futures market and the fat cattle market in Greeley. Thirdly, the packer is the one who must put up the margin money involved in the hedging operation. This allows the feeder to concentrate on producing the best possible product, and keeps him from being involved in, you might say, "playing" the market.

When the feeder determines to hedge his livestock, he is letting someone else assume the risk. He is also letting someone else assume the bulk of the profit if the market should turn out to be a profitable type of affair at the particular time.

I would like to close by telling you what I think about the future of the cattle industry. I have already established that I am certainly no expert. I believe that there are certain things happening in the cattle business that may be of interest to you here. You have all heard of consumer boycotts, the higher price of food, etc. True, many food items have gone up, but let us look in particular at the beef situation. The same might apply to many other agricultural items. The current retail prices for beef are too low to allow everyone that has to handle that beef to make a profit. The price level is such that there are just not enough dollars to split between the retailer, the packer, the feeder, and the rancher for them all to cover their costs of production, let alone to make a profit. It is rather obvious that the retailer, the chain store if you wish, is in the best bargaining position for making a profit. Their profits are not higher than should be in my opinion. I wish they were higher. It would be easier to get along with them. The packing industry is next in line, and their profit picture is bleak. On the average, they are still sufficient to cover their cost of operation. Eventually it gets back to the feeder and the rancher to split what is left, and there just is not enough money to split so both operations can be profitable simultaneously. The rancher has consistently lost money for the last five or six years. He has stayed in business basically because his land values have inflated. He has been able to refinance his land. This is apparently coming to an end. The rancher is now faced with the prospect of being forced out of business. To make ends meet, he is selling too many of his brood cows and replacement heifers for slaughter. This is creating a small surplus of beef now, but it endangers future beef production potential. This cycle of the cattle business must soon end. We will see higher prices in the years to come, and we will very well see shortages of beef in the not too distant future. The consumers must soon realize that the cattle industry in America has been subsidizing them, and that this will have to stop if they are to expect the quality and quantity of beef to which they have become accustomed.

I hope higher prices will occur, in the markets of America, whether that market place be the Mercantile Exchange in Chicago, the A & P Supermarket in Teaneck, New Jersey, the auction sale ring in Dodge City, Kansas, or the feed lot in Greeley, Colorado.

Paper presented at the Livestock and Meats Futures Study Conference-Chicago on November 30, 1966.

This Little Pig Went to Which Market?

by
Lee Schuster
Schuster Farms, Clinton, Missouri

Pigs are my obsession,
My life and my profession,
I find them so appealing —
So round and fat and squealing.
At night when I can't sleep
I count pigs instead of sheep.

The time for your conference is completely in keeping with views I'll be expressing this afternoon. You realize by the introduction of a live hog option that things are changing fast in the industry.

We have been in the hog business in Northwest Missouri since 1839. My great-great grandfather homesteaded a tract of land from the government under the Platte Purchase. In those days Cincinnati was referred to as "Porkopolis" and the forerunner of our toll road (in those days called a "Pike") was coming into being with the colorful drover pushing his herd of pigs to the terminal for slaughter. The program was somewhat refined over the next forty years with the Civil War bringing into existence major packers locating primarily in Chicago. The basic design of the mammoth terminal plant evolved in this period and until the last decade, was little changed. Terminals developed simply because each was located at a terminating point of a railroad. Hogs were railed in to large metropolitan areas for processing, and more often than not, consumption.

Thus, the terminal served as a useful purpose as long as it was more economical to bring the raw product into metropolitan centers. The terminals up to the early 1950's were receiving close to 90% of the total kill and rightfully became the pricing centers determining what 100 pounds of live hog was worth. Chicago, befitting earlier marketing tradition was the center of the packing industry, not only for killing but also pricing. It was the headquarters of major packers. Rumblings of change were in the air moving into the fifties. There is no clear-cut indication as to where we will end up in the progression of changes.

Let us then, as a guideline, bring our brief history into hog marketing up to date. Trucks, have evolved as a mode of conveyance leaving little advantage for a killing plant to be located at a rail terminal. Terminals with traffic congestion, antiquated plants, and valuable real estate have hastened the exodus of processing to the country. Chicago, is a prime example, kills no hogs now, in contrast to an earlier dominant position. As a matter of interest, the terminal marketing system during 1966 received less than one hog in four and, if this trend continues, (with apologies to those in the audience who might be affiliated with this system) I see little reason for the terminal to even be in existence in its present form ten years hence. I am not here, to argue whether this is right or wrong. I am well aware of the pricing implications and other difficulties involved in what is bound to be a rather painful transition.

Up to now we have been talking about ancient history. Let's move up to the fall of 1967. I have ten generalizations which might serve as guidelines for industry direction.

1. We are in the strictest sense, becoming a coordinated industry with pipeline communications from housewife to retailer, to packer, to producer, more open now than anytime in the past. This can't help but facilitate communications as well as change.

2. Packers are becoming smaller. The big four of yesteryear are handling a much smaller percentage of total kill, and they no longer dominate the industry. New smaller efficient plants are popping up hither and yon in the country close to areas of production rather than consumption. These plants are being run with high degrees of autonomy and are geared to deal on a more direct basis with producers.

3. Producers are becoming larger. We have a dramatic decrease in total number of farms in the United States, but this is even more pronounced in the swine industry. The number of farms raising pigs is dropping at double the rate of decrease in all farms.

4. Even though units are becoming bigger, we still have a long way to go. The average pig farm is now selling only 80 head per year. Nevertheless, this is double the figure of ten years ago. If current projected trends continue, we will be thinking in terms of a typical hog farm marketing between one and two thousand head ten years hence. We now have a large number in this bracket as evidenced by recent Hog Management surveys.

5. As production units become larger, killing units become smaller, and more localized, each will get to know one another on a more direct basis.

6. We will see continued acceleration of some form of grade and yield purchase. That is a scheme wherein animals are evaluated and paid for after slaughter. Many will disagree with this contention, so a word of explanation might be in order.

I mentioned that new efficient plants are springing up in the country. The "Old Jonahs" at the terminal are having trouble adapting to grade and yield purchases, i.e., (tatooing or maintaining lot identity, carcass weighing, and so forth), but as new plants are built all are incorporating these innovations; so whether the producer chooses to sell on grade and yield or not is of little consequence. Packers are interested in evaluating the job their buyers do on the hoof, and will be developing their own judging standards at the plant. The packer at the terminal deals with a commission man rather than producer. In the country, dealings are direct with the farmer.

Mr. Edwards will be speaking to you this evening, and will possibly touch on two new Wilson plants at Cherokee, Iowa, and Logansport, Indiana. Both of these are geared for ready assimilation of kill data. Let us, for sake of argument, assume that I'm a producer of two thousand head near Logansport (roughly a straight-truck load) per week during the year. Assume that I choose to sell to Wilson, but not on grade and yield. Wilson management, however, being amongst the most progressive in the industry, wants to know how my hogs grade. They will be evaluating my animals during the kill to see how they stack up in the cooler. If my hogs are the desirable kind, I'll be paid accordingly, on the next delivery. The converse would also be true if they are not of the grade desirable. For lack of a better term I'd call this delayed grade and yield.

7. Pricing, as this trend accelerates, will find traditional terminal quotations inadequate. I might mention as an aside that the Chicago Mercantile Exchange certainly gives undue weight to what is often a scratch top figure quoted on one or two hundred head here in Chicago. A run of only four thousand head out of a day's commercial slaughter in excess of two hundred thousand should hardly be a market establisher.

8. In view of the above, new methods of pricing will evolve. The one which holds particular appeal to me is the delayed payment system based on value of cuts.

9. All of the above points will accelerate means of communication mentioned earlier. Packers will routinely council producers who supply them. They will advise a processor about changes in consumer preferences, market weights, yields and so forth. I might stop here briefly to pay special tribute to John Morrell and Company. The job they have done in their extension program at their subsidiary — Hunter Packing Company in East St. Louis — along these lines is most commendable.

10. My final generalization is that the entire industry is ready for all this. With all of above points as a springboard, I would like to wade into the gist of today's discussion. First, we might generalize that up until a year ago, hog producers were completely production oriented. Pick up any farm magazine dated prior to 1966, and many were the articles you would find on breeding, disease, nutrition, management, housing, and so forth. The major emphasis was on numbers rather than on quality. The main measure of success was how many, rather than how good were the pigs in each litter. Packers conceded that a quality marketing program at retail level has merit, but complained that it was useless to start such a project for lack of the kind of animals needed in volume to make this program work. Farmers argued that it was useless to produce quality because they didn't

get paid for it. Not so now, as we read of packer success with prestige lines which are commanding premiums in the market place. As this happens, packers are finding that they can pay for quality. As a tribute to my provisioner friends, this is just what they are doing. No longer can the producer use the argument that it is useless to produce a quality product because of lack of financial reward. The day is rapidly approaching when not only will quality be well rewarded, but the junk will be proportionately discounted. A token 25 cents per cwt. of yesterday will widen to an impressive $1.50 or $2.00 of tomorrow. This, I predict, will shape up the industry faster than anything else.

Those of you from the Mercantile Exchange I am sure, are shifting in your chairs at this point. This might be an interesting little dissertation on the swine industry, but it certainly does not offer any concrete suggestions as to how the open interest of five or six hundred live hog contracts might be increased to the 17,000 level we now have on the pork bellies, or the 18,500 open interest on live cattle. Though, we have looked at what has happened, and what is happening, you might agree with my viewpoint as to what will happen. I mentioned that producers are becoming aware of market muscle shifting the degree of emphasis away from production to market orientation. The American National Cattlemen's Association is devoting its efforts towards establishing beef needs of the future before the bull is ever turned in with the cows, or for those of you who are not animal husbandrymen, a lapse of two and a half years. Those of you, who concern yourselves with the shell egg contract, are doubtless aware of similar producer cooperation in the banding together for marketing of eggs on a regional basis. This sort of thinking is evolving rapidly in the swine industry. Individual producers are small in the overall picture. As mentioned in my introduction, we are marketing 15,000 hogs per year, but this is nothing in the overall picture. I was amused several weeks ago when a broker with whom we do business in Chicago was inquiring into our marketing plans for the upcoming week. He was attempting to determine what the market might be expected to do. If we were to have, stretching our imagination, all our animals ready for market on one day, we could just about handle an average run at Omaha and Kansas City.

Thus, you can readily see that the industry is highly fragmented. Let us for arguments sake say, that I was able to pool my production with others in our community and come up with sufficient volume to be of real interest to a packer. Now, let us further assume that volume was located near my base of operations. Suppose it has (a small packing plant) established a quality image in a given market with a given medium-sized chain. The packer knows that his market demands 14-16 pound loins, 16-18 pound hams, and hogs which consistently cut 54%. Is it not conceivable that I, as a producer, could coordinate a breeding program which would tailor this hog for this packer and retail affiliation? Is it not further conceivable that all these hogs could be fed on the same feeding program offering another assurance of uniformity? Is it not further conceivable that we could all use standardized management procedures with planned breeding to assure an even flow to the market place?

You are "darned tooting" all this is a possibility; and gentlemen, I firmly believe it will come to pass. Who benefits from all this?

A. *Producer:* The packer has a specific market for a quality product before it is bought and can consequently pay more.

B. *Packer:* Procurements costs are lowered. With hogs in his hip pocket, he does not have to fool with an antiquated terminal, costly country buying stations, or high-prices buyers running up and down the road bidding against each other. He knows exactly what he is buying from past experience and it's not "a pig in the poke."

C. *Retailer:* He can in all honesty say to the housewife that the pound of bacon she buys this week will taste and look the same as last week's purchase. He can promote pork as a consistent high quality product.

D. *Housewife:* She develops brand allegiance no longer thinking of pork as cord-wood or simply a commodity to be moved at a price. Talk to any of your wives, and you will quickly learn that the biggest complaint now voiced against bacon, ham, chops, sausage, and so on, is a lack of uniformity. Broiler consumption has had a phenomenal growth based largely upon uniform (if mediocre) quality.

The one fly in the ointment is pricing. I must readily concede that this is so, and herein lies a golden opportunity for futures pricing.

Believe it or not, Producers, do not relish thirty dollar hogs because we know good and well that we are sowing seeds of a seventeen dollar market later on. Wide price swings play havoc with financial planning, and the industry is moving in the direction of searching for price stability either via hedging directly or contracting. As I see it, we could not care less which direction is finally taken. Hedging gives you the business directly with the producer, while future contracting means that you will probably be dealing with the packer. Perhaps, if we ultimately decide on a pricing scheme for pork rather than pigs, we will be trading in hams, as well as loins and shoulders.

What are some of the pitfalls of the live hog contract? First, this market seems basically predicated on what happens at the Chicago terminal on a day-to-day basis. From a producer's viewpoint, this is a dangerous situation. Better producers turning out better animals are going direct. Poorer producers (Many close to retirement) are loyal to the terminal, and they ship less desirable animals. This inferior quality in turn becomes a basing point for pricing of better animals at the plant. Thus the quality producer has not gained too much even if he gets a quality payment. The base from which he is paid is lower to start with. This man is ripe for a more equitable price determination: but, as in the case with the packing industry, he is not quite sure where to turn.

I am affiliated with a company which has been wrestling with this problem for a year and a half now. I think it is significant that during this time, two packers have actually put people on their staffs to explore future contracting. This is a red hot subject; and, although everybody talks about it, in reality we must concede that nobody has done very much about it.

Invariably, in discussions on this subject, the CME Live Hog Contract comes under consideration. Invariably, it is dismissed

[177]

with the observation that: "You can't get anything done on the exchange due to lack of volume and liquidity.

Fully realizing that this is a chicken-egg problem, I thought it might be helpful to offer my own observations on this contract however distressing it may be:

1. The very success of pork bellies has been a deterrent to the live hog trade. Much of the same might be said in reverse with the now defunct beef carcass trade losing out to live cattle. Give us a good sustained bull market in live hogs, or a lapse of activity in bellies, and I think this might take care of some of this problem.

2. Delivery is not a problem. Several years ago I was on a panel with Mr. Harris prior to the first cattle deliveries. He stated at that time that the only hurdle cattle yet had would be mechanics of successful delivery. It is now history, of course, that this did not prove to be a problem. I think I can speak with some authority on the hog contract, having delivered five thousand head in a week's time to many men represented in this room. As an aside, I might mention that it was a hectic week to say the least. To the best of my knowledge, however, the problems were all mechanical, and virtually all parties concerned came out OK. The thing which impressed me most was that it all worked out quite logically with Schuster Farms, as producers, being on the short side of the contract, and longs being either packers or order buyers.

3. Producer interest is not going to be sparked in a downtown brokerage office. You won't get him there in the first place, and if by accident you did, he would not be comfortable. This is going to be a personal selling job by people who are livestock orientated rather then someone who has been a specialist in loose lard, hams, hides, frozen eggs, toms, or any one of the other commodities which has dropped by the wayside.

4. The financial community has not been sold. Agricultural bankers, Production Credit Association managers, and credit men representing feed companies could give this contract a tremendous boost if they were sold on the basis of reducing inherent risk in a livestock loan.

5. At the risk of throwing a cobra and a mongoose together, I would further suggest a coordinated effort with the Board of

[178]

Trade to emphasize hedging costs of production via corn and Soy Bean Oil Meal and ultimate product via live hogs, cattle, shell eggs, etc.

6. The long side of the market as a hedge, to the best of my knowledge, has never been mentioned to the producer. Let us assume that I have hogs now at 220 to sell, but I anticipate the market will be higher in December because of Christmas ham business or what have you. I know full well that my cost of gain is uneconomical beyond 220 pounds, December option is in line with the cash market, but I still feel there is another dollar on the up side. What better hedge than to sell cash hogs and buy December contracts?

Hold on, though. I didn't intend to come to Chicago to throw out trading philosophies to the pros. My main mission in visiting with you, today, was to convey some of the marketing philosophy we feel is evolving in the country.

As a producer I very much want the live hog option to live and grow. As members of the Mercantile you feel the same. In summation, I would like to recap with a concluding observation. One which has a definite implication for producers, packers, and those who would provide assistance in evolving an orderly pricing mechanism fair to all parties.

The terminal is fading as a marketing center and nothing has come forth to date to provide a pricing substitute. Producers, as they become bigger, and packers as they become more localized, will get to know one another better. As this happens a coordinated sales effort tailored for local markets will be facilitated ultimately which will bring the four segments of the market closer together namely the hog man, processor, retailer, and consumer.

The time is ripe for future pricing and contracting. The swine industry is becoming increasingly sophisticated and market, rather than production, oriented. As this evolves, the challenge to you gentlemen will be to find a place in this industry of transition. It is not only exciting but it will promise financial rewards. At this stage, nobody has an answer. There are many who are wrestling with the problem, and I would like to think that the live hog contract will fit into the final solution.

Paper presented at the Live Hog Futures Study Conference-Chicago on November 16, 1967.

The first "Porker" to be delivered on a CME Futures Contract

Part V

Some General Observations Relevant to
Trading in Futures

Some Economic Myths of our Times

by
Don Paarlberg
Purdue University

First, let me commend the Chicago Mercantile Exchange for holding this conference. This conference as an effort to improve the functioning of the market for the most important of all agricultural commodities, cattle; to assist in the process of price discovery; and to make possible the shifting of risk from those who wish to avoid it to those who elect to bear it.

This is a major undertaking, and a constructive one. The thing I like about this approach is that it is progressive. We who believe in the market economy believe that there must be innovation and change if the market is to be at its best. Insurance was such an innovation. The official grading of commodities was another. Futures trading was another, and the adaption of this institution to additional commodities is yet another.

But, let me speak this word of warning: When you have successfully worked out the technical details of futures trading in live cattle, there will remain another great unsolved problem, which is the lack of public understanding. And if they don't understand it, how will they accept or support it? A.G. Osgood, vice president of the Harris Trust and Savings Bank, facetiously defines futures trading as "buying and selling what you never had and did not pay for at more than it cost-" How will the people understand such an operation? Of today's voting public, only about 10% have had as much as one formal course in economics. Imagine the mathematical competence of the population if only 10% of the people have ever studied arithmetic!

The esoteric aspects of market operations may not have been particularly troublesome in years past, when we were, in effect,

[183]

governed by those we called "the wise, the rich and the well-born." But we now live in what has been called "the age of the Common Man." If the common man doesn't understand the market, he is not likely to defend or support it. He may, in fact, tear it down, and replace it with centralized decision-making, as he already has in one-third of the world. Your chairman has mentioned the fact that I formerly served as economic advisor in the federal government. While in that post, I was impressed with the generally low level of economic literacy in the country, and with the handicaps thereby imposed on the functioning of the economic system. I drew up a list of economic myths, deeply and widely held erroneous beliefs which jeopardize the functioning of a free economy. Some of these I wish to share with you. Here are two:

(1) The myth that if someone gains, someone loses.
(2) The myth of heroes and villains.

But before I comment on these individual myths, let me say a word about economic mythology in general. Economics is a mystery to many. Stand on a busy street corner some weekday morning and watch the people streaming by, each occupied with with his own affairs. Where are they bound? What are they about? How did they get their present jobs? Who had the forethought to produce the goods with which their needs might be met? Pick out one of them and ask yourself, "What it his probable income? Why not more? Why that much?"

Or go into a modern supermarket. Here are some 5,000 food items on display, each marked with a price. What forces led to the production of all of these items? Why does some particular cut of meat sell at $1.05 per pound? Why not $.90 or $1.25? December cattle futures at the Chicago Mercantile Exchange were recently quoted at $27.50. Why that price? Why not more, or less? The census lists some 1,800 different occupations in the United States, including 264,000 stenographers, 330,000 plumbers and 38,000 airline pilots. How did we happen to get approximately the right number of people to fill these jobs? Ask these questions of the people themselves, and you would get a variety of answers, partly based on things wholly personal, and partly based on economic mythology. That there might be undergirding principles — economic laws — which explain and coordinate this multiplicity of activities would be a novel thought to many. The whole process, marvelously integrated and interdependent as it is, seems without unifying principle.

If someone were to ask, "Why do people behave as they do?" he would be told, "They do what they themselves have chosen," a reply that leaves much unexplained. How does 200-million people, operate without central direction, make the proper choices? How would you explain the voluntary system, with each person freely choosing his own job and making his own decisions? The principles which support it are not understood. To many people, economics is beyond comprehension.

People do not like to be without comprehension. They like to understand things, to have some belief which permits an observed event to take on meaning. This craving finds outlet in the myths which people create to explain their condition, or their hopes, or the events they see about them. The belief does not necessarily have to be true, some fragment of truth will suffice. There is not ordinarily a disposition to place the myth to the test. To do so would be to risk the security of mind which the myth provides, which is the very purpose of its being. The motive which leads to the propagation of a myth is not the scientific quest for fact; it is a subconscious desire for a personally acceptable answer to the question, "Why?"

Thus, there arise fragmentary and inconsistent explanations for observed events. I shall deal with two of these economic myths.

The myth that probably causes the most difficulty in the field of public policy is this: the belief that if two people engage in a transaction and one of them is seen to gain thereby, it must follow that the other has lost. One man's gain is felt to be another man's loss. This myth is extended to encompass whole groups. Economics is looked on as a game of dice: "No greater value is carried away than is brought in." To put it concretely: Members of the Chicago Mercantile Exchange deal in farm commodities. The myth has it that if members of the exchange are seen to make money, they must have made it at the expense of the farmers. This is the myth. It needs the best analysis we can give it.

Consider two common characterizations of the exchange process. In the first one, the average citizen drives past the suburban home of some wealthy businessman, notes the huge lawn, the lovely landscaping and the late-model car parked in the driveway. "Nobody," says he to himself "could get that much money without taking it away from somebody else!"

In the second characterization, this same citizen buys a pair of shoes at a drygoods store owned by the same businessman. "Thank you!" he says, as he receives his shoes. "Thank you!" says the clerk as he rings up the money. Is this exchange of "thank you's" a mere matter of form? Or does it express something intuitively or even subconsciously felt by these two people? In any case, buyer and seller have cause to be pleased with this voluntary transaction, and to thank each other. Each received an item of greater value *to him* than the value of the item with which he parted. The buyer preferred the shoes to the money; for the seller the reverse was true. So both gained by the exchange.

Which of these two characterizations is the more accurate, the citizen's allegation that he has been exploited, or his courteous acknowledgement of a service rendered? Is the exchange process mutually advantageous? Or is it a matter of exploitation? The myth says that trade is exploitation — exploitation of the weaker by the stronger, of the smaller by the larger, of the poorer by the more wealthy.

Once this myth is embraced, many things follow. All profits become evil, all business is viewed as a scramble to take something away from somebody else, and all wealth is thought to have been accumulated by exploitation. Any nation which really accepts this myth will either confiscate or closely regulate its private property. It will inject government deeply into the marketing and pricing process, and will substitute centralized decision-making for the operation of free markets. The fact that the United States has gone so far in this direction is evidence that the myth is widely held. The danger to a free society bred by this myth is subtle and great.

It is clear that as specialization and trade take place, the total volume of wealth increases. With widespread trading, the net worth of the country is rising. The gross evidence is contrary to the myth. Experience shows that when people are free

[186]

to exchange goods, they invariably do so. If, as the myth would have it, one party or the other is victimized in the process, then it would be most extraordinary that the total population would so consistently lay itself open to injury. Nothing that I have said denies the fact that exploitation *does* sometimes exist, that on certain occasions someone's gain is someone else's loss. This is the fragment of truth which keeps the myth alive.

The great myths of literature are liberally supplied with heroes and villains. In fact, the essence of mythology is the personification of events. When the volcano erupted, Vulcan was at work; when the waves rose, Poseidon was troubled; if events were against man, it was because some God had thwarted him.

One of the great myths of economics is the personification of hopes and problems; the explanation of events in terms of individual acts. This myth has immense appeal:

(1.) It simplifies complex matters.

(2.) It permits instantaneous appraisal of current proposals.

(3.) It provides outlet for the human desire to extoll virtue and to castigate villainy.

The utility of instant identification will be attested by anyone who has watched a television program. The audience wants to know who to pull for, and whom to be against; our stylized Westerns readily accommodate this wish. Heroes wear white hats or ride white horses. Villains are identified by scowl or speech. One can switch on the set in the middle of a program and be current as to the plot in a moment. So with the economic myth. Should the citizen favor some proposal? This is not a difficult matter. He identified his hero, and notes where the hero stands on the question; if the hero is for it, the citizen feels safe in supporting it. More likely, the citizen decides what he himself is for and attaches the hero's label to any public figure who concurs.

Heroes and villains can be individual persons, political parties, vocational group or causes. They come in various sizes and categories. Among individual heroes there is the elder-statesman type, the man of action, the rough-hewn man of the people, the man of principle, and many others. For villains, one can take his choice. There is the pawn of the vested interest, the unscrupulous

[187]

man, the expedient man, and the man who is simply uninformed. Men in public life become type-casted in one or another of these categories, tabbed and labeled for instant recognition. The man who accidentally acquires a hero's billing is fortunate indeed; the man who has the misfortune to be cast as a villain can spend the rest of his life trying to detach the label.

How accurate are these labels? Not very accurate, obviously. Most men and most organized groups are too complex to be accurately tabbed as villainous or heroic. There must be enough authenticity in the labeling process to make the whole operation credible. This need not be very much.

What caused the Great Depression? The myth says that Herbert Hoover was responsible, though a search of the literature of the 1930's turned up 43 different explanations, put forward by responsible people, for that complex event.

Why does the farm population keep declining? The myth says that farms are being liquidated by the Secretary of Agriculture, and this despite the documented fact that the technological revolution is responsible.

What causes wages to rise: The myth delegates sole responsibility to the labor unions, despite the fact that the trend began long before there were any unions and despite the fact that wages rise in non-union industries as well as in organized plants.

Who is for fiscal responsibility? The Republicans, says the myth, though the Grand Old Party can count some great spenders among its number. Who is for the common man? The Democrats, says the myth, despite the fact that a large sector of the party represents the privileged part of the society.

Who are the heroes saluted by those now called liberals? Among others, the myths lists Jefferson, Jackson, and Franklin Roosevelt. Certainly Jefferson would be ill at ease with the programs now offered under the liberal label. Who are the heroes recognized by those now called conservatives? Hamilton, Lincoln, and Robert Taft are among them, though Lincoln certainly frightened some of the conservatives of his time.

Certain causes come to be identified in economic mythology as heroic. The fight against monopoly is such a cause. The fight against inflation is another. The fight for labor is yet another.

Another is the fight for pure food, as witnessed by the "cranberry crisis" of 1959, when the Department of Health, Education, and Welfare prohibited the sale of berries containing such infinitesimal quantities of herbicide that a person would have to consume 13 tons in order to experience injury.

Some causes become identified in economic mythology as villainous. The desire of farmers to employ seasonal workers younger than the legal minimum age is such a villainous cause, despite the willingness and the ability of young people to engage in such labor. Importation of labor from Mexico is also villainous. And, make no mistake about it, trading on the commodity exchanges is identified (by some people) as contrary to the public interest.

Sometimes a cause will shift from one category to another. Protecting American industry from foreign imports was once heroic, but is now villainous. The cause of agriculture was once heroic, but the city man, with his far greater number of votes, finds the merit of his cause increasing relative to that of his country cousin.

Of course there are some authentic heroes and some genuine villains, and these are often discovered. The country's leaders do indeed make decisions which have far-reaching consequences, for good and ill. It is appropriate for the people to try to take the measure of their leaders, and to appraise their acts. The problem comes with oversimplification, to which the leader himself is often a part. He tries to receive credit for more than he really does. It is a matter of poetic justice, perhaps, that he also, then, be charged with responsibility for more than his share of the things that go wrong.

Demythologizing economics is a difficult task. A professor may spend a full class period with 30 students analyzing some particular piece of economic life with all its complexities and interrelationships. But that night some political figure, in a five-minute telecast for a nationwide audience, will explain the whole thing simply and understandably in terms of heroes and villains.

In the myth of heroes and villains, we have an unfair basis for judging individuals; a method by which the public engages in self-delusion on a grand scale, and a threat to marketing institutions like the Mercantile Exchange.

How should we, who are concerned with the proper functioning of the market economy, deal with these myths? Must we accept them and live with them? Has our interdependent society become so complex that economic understanding is impossible? I say, "NO!" Economic education *is* necessary. I quote Thomas Jefferson: "I know of no safe depository of the ultimate powers of society but the people themselves; and if we think them not enlightened enough to exercise their control with a wholesome discretion, the remedy is not to take it from them, but to inform their discretion by education." Abraham Lincoln said, "Let the people know the facts and the country will be saved."

Our defense of the market system must be intellignt and progressive, not archaic or reactionary. The central objective should be freedom. The word freedom is here used in the constitutional sense — a concept which so limits the freedom of each as to maximize the freedom of all. A serious error comes from considering freedom to by synonymous with license, the total absence of restraint. A better concept of freedom is that it be closely tied to responsibility. The plain citizen puts it simply: "Your freedom ends where my rights begin." The more responsibility is self imposed, the less restraint will have to be supplied from outside. Certainly, it is within the province of government to prescribe the general conditions under which access to the market is to be available — conditions related to health, public safety, the national security, patent rights, and the like. But arbitrary exclusion from the market does not fit the criterion.

To argue for free access to the market is to contemplate an active, but not a dominant role for government. This role is to improve the functioning of the exchange system, to place a floor over the pit of disaster, to help the individual equip himself better for his task as a decision-maker, and to see that the market functions as an enlightened institution.

Many who believe in the market system allow themselves to be backed into a corner and forced to defend an institution which is not at all what they advocate. They unintentionally take on the defense, not of the free market, but a caricature thereof. They are maneuvered into defending the free market, not as it is or as it could be, but as it once was or as its adversaries contend it should be.

What is here advocated is a market free from manipulation, free from misrepresentation, free from gross ignorance, and free from senseless gyration as well as free from government domination. It means the kind of market that intelligent people are capable of creating in the modern day.

Advocacy of access to the market need not and should not be a doctrinaire position which renounces all of the enlightened marketing institutions that have developed since the turn of the century, though adversaries of the free market try to force defenders into such a position.

If the advantages of the market are to be retained, the myth which makes the market synonymous with exploitation will have to be dispelled. If the abuses of the market are to be avoided, the market must be a more enlightened institution. In any case, economic education must occur. The market system at least deserves to be understood before it is condemned, and presently, it is being condemned without proper understanding.

Students of biology learn that there are three distinct circumstances within which different species exist together. There is the parasitic relationship, as when the mistletoe attaches itself to the oak and lives by exploiting its host. There is the competitive relationship, as when corn and weeds compete with each other for moisture and sunlight. There is the symbiotic relationship, by which two species help each other, as do the bee and the clover.

Failure to understand these relationships has led man to drive to the point of extinction certain species which were wrongly felt to be harmful. We now discover that relationships thought to be parasitic are not so in fact and that the number of symbiotic relationships is far greater than we thought to be true.

Likewise, the myth that the tradesman is parasitic has placed in jeopardy an institution which holds immense possibilities for improving levels of living. The need is to dispel this myth and make the market an even more effective instrument.

If the Chicago Mercantile Exchange is to be successful in the trading of live cattle, the technical details of such trading will have to be worked out, as perhaps they have already been, and the market will have to perform in a constructive fashion as perhaps it is already doing. That will be necessary. But it will not be sufficient. In the long run, whether cattle trading succeeds, or whether the Mercantile Exchange continues to exist, or whether the market economy survives will depend on the public understanding and acceptance of these institutions. The myths that jeopardize the market will have to be dispelled. At stake is the economic system itself. The big job is education.

Other Economic writers have taken pains to prove "That if someone gains in a transaction, someone must lose." The readers may refer to the book which inspired the Technocrats of the thirties entitled, The Engineers and the Price System" by Thorstein Veblen, or to Bakken's "Theory of Markets and Marketing" in which the author categorically states, "In a true market transaction one man's gain is another man's loss." This basic precept is elucidated in chapter 10 of his book. A number of other writers would take sharp exception to Paarlberg's thesis.   Editors note

Paper presented at Live Cattle Futures Study Conference-Chicago on September 8, 1966.

Changing Emphases in Futures Markets and Ways and Means to Improve Them

by
Thomas A. Hieronymus
University of Illinois

Cattle, hogs, and fresh egg futures markets are new departures in the field of futures trading. Two of these new markets established by the Chicago Mercantile Exchange are working and the third is not. I wish to look at some of the new concepts and at the things that may be needed to assist in the success of the new markets.

At the outset, I should like to commend the Chicago Mercantile Exchange for the innovations made in recent years. These have been forward-looking steps that have already enhanced the position of the exchange (and the value of the memberships). You should continue to look ahead, to change, and to improve.

New Concepts. Although we have long looked at futures markets as risk shifting and pricing arrangements, they are, in the final analysis, financial institutions. Their business is furnishing equity capital. Historically, futures markets have been mainly concerned with furnishing capital for carrying inventories of stored commodities. This has been accomplished by hedging in which risks of price change associated with stored commodities have been shifted from hedger to speculator. This shifting has enabled the hedgers to borrow from the banks at prime rates of interest. The equity capital with which price changes are absorbed is furnished by the speculators who buy the hedges.

The new game, recently started, is the equity financing of production. It has been brought about by the increasing commercialization of agricultural production that has greatly reduced the abiltiy of primary producers to carry the risks of price change.

[193]

FUTURES TRADING IN LIVESTOCK

Agriculture is changing rapidly. Production is becoming more specialized, concentrated and commercialized. Out-of-pocket costs are becoming a higher proportion of total costs. Producers are using an increasing proportion of total costs. Producers are using an increasing proportion of borrowed capital. Farms, those engaged in poultry and livestock production in particular, are becoming factories that buy a high proportion of their inputs. They are operating on increasingly thin margins. Thus, change in the selling price has a major effect on net return. A moderate change in the price can easily halve or double the net profit. Because of these changes, primary producers are losing their ability to carry risks of price change in advance of the production process and are looking for ways to produce at firm contracted prices.

This method of — reducing producer risks — is coming to the forefront, is forward pricing through futures trading. As this system grows and expands, products will be produced at firm prices for delivery on completion of production. As this occurs the capital to finance production will be forthcoming at minimum interest rates.

The equity capital necessary to carry the risks of price uncertainty and variability is furnished by speculators. Studies of the older futures markets indicate that speculators furnished this capital at very low or even negative rates of return. It appears that speculators, as a group, lose money or at best break even minus the cost of commissions. They do this because of the leverage that minimum margin requirements makes possible. They hazard a small amount of money in exchange for the chance to make a large amount.

As capital to finance producers is furnished at minimum rates, the competitiveness of producers is increased. They are freed to concentrate on efficiency of production. A workable system of forward pricing of production will lower cost just as a hedging system for stored commodities has increased marketing efficiency. This is economic progress and contributes to the welfare of the nation.

The most important single problem in agriculture is the expansion of markets. As markets for products expand, more resources, especially people, can be retained to carry on agricultural production. Our agricultural markets are no longer based on the necessity to consume food; rather they are based on the desire to eat better food. The markets in which we sell no longer need to consume only those foods that can be produced efficiently. Our productive capacity, can direct the marketing production system to furnish the products that are most wanted. Agriculture now responds to orders from consumers. At such a time, market growth is dependent upon good merchandising and new product development.

Price stability is essential to good merchandising programs. One problem that we have had in the past in increasing consumer expenditures is variable prices. This has been, and is, particularly true of the livestock and poultry sectors. Price stability should be maximized. It is not possible to totally stabilize price. There are vagaries of nature, changes in technology, changes in consumer behavior, and inadequacies of knowledge that make some price variation inevitable if prices are to direct the production-consumption system. Yet maximum price stability must be our goal. The fundamental goal of futures trading must be a set of prices that so effectively guides production and consumption that prices remain stable. Futures markets live on price variability. Their goal must be to put themselves out of business.

Speculators. The equity capital for production is furnished by speculators to the extent that producers forward contract through futures markets. By doing this the speculators gain control of production. The forward prices that are established by trading between producers and speculators order and direct production. As the distant futures prices are bid up by the speculators, production is increased. And as they are lower, production is retarded. Speculators control prices to the extent that producers and buyers contract forward.

The responsibility for price stability rests on speculators in futures markets. The quality of the job that they do will ultimately determine the success or failure of the markets in achieving the broader objective of price stability.

It is true that speculators will carry the risks of the price variation, sometimes profiting and sometimes losing, whether they do a good job of pricing or not. But this only partially im-

[195]

proves the performance of the system. Major attention must be paid to improving the quality of the job that speculators do.

The intention of every speculator is to make money. The success of the speculator depends upon his ability to forecast prices. There are other considerations in successful speculation, but the forecasting of equilibrium prices is fundamental and determining in a fully competitive market. They must analyze the quantities that will be consumed at a series of prices at specified times in the future — specifically the delivery months. They must analyze the quantities that will be furnished at a series of prices at the same times in the future. The intercept of these two schedules, demand and supply, is the resultant forecast. They must not be unduly influenced to the extent that they project the current supply, demand, and price situation into forecasts of prices at future times, however. In contrast to the inventory hedging markets, these new markets are truly forward contracts markets; they are supply determining.

To the victor belongs the spoils; to the more skilled forecasters will go the profits and to the less skilled will go the losses. As the speculators, as a group, become more skilled, the less it will be necessary to adjust prices as the forward contracts mature and the more stable prices will become; and less will be the remaining profit opportunities.

What the market must do. All of this is by way of a preface to what the market must do to achieve its full potential. I shall list two principal things. First, it should teach forward contracting through futures trading to producers, buyers, processors, and distributors. The history of most futures markets is that they are built on forward contracting — hedging; that the need to shift risks comes first and where there is risk and price variability speculation follows.

This is a big teaching job and requires a large and continuing effort. Producers in particular must be taught to contract forward, the way in which their trading activities are related to their production operations, the relationship of *their* cash prices to futures prices, and how to account and relate profits and losses. This is what this study conference has been about. More importantly, they must be taught not to speculate. The exchange and such public agencies as the Cooperative Extension Service can do some of this teaching, but the bulk of the effort must be made by the commission merchants. They are the only ones who can do the job because they are the ones who directly profit from the generation of new business.

Second, the market must help speculators make money. Speculators must be furnished a flow of information that can be used in forecasting and they must be taught to use the information in making forecasts. Unfortunately, before these things can be accomplished someone must learn what information is pertinent and how to use it. Then the speculators must be taught to avoid mistakes in capital management, from letting mistakes in forecasting become too expansive, and from over-trading. (This) latter is necessary if the lives of the speculators are to be preserved long enough for them to learn to forecast; keep them alive first and then teach them to forecast.

What the market offers. The development of the new livestock futures offers opportunities for improvement and profit to many segments of the livestock and meat production, processing; and distribution industry.

First, the market offers producers an opportunity to contract forward at firm prices; an opportunity to produce at profitable rates of return, or to refuse to produce. It takes the age old uncertainty of gross revenue out of production. In the past, studies of factors affecting the profitability of livestock enterprises have indicated selling price or feeding margin as the single most important consideration. The ability of the producer to speculate has been a major factor in success or failure. Price uncertainty can now be substantially reduced and nearly ended by the use of futures markets. Producers can now turn full attention to increasing efficiency of production. This particularly includes the opportunities to expand production units without restriction by risk bearing ability and capital rationing. Second, the futures markets offer producers as a group an opportunity to stabilize production variations and increase the size of their markets. Increased production efficiency will lead to lower cost which in turn leads to lower prices and larger markets.

[197]

Livestock production has been notorious in the past for seasonal and cyclical variation. Production responses have been based on *current* market prices, and feeding ratios. As producers learn to respond to forward prices, expanding as profitable forward prices are offered and contracting as forwards prices are not profitable, the cobweb cycles should be reduced. The complete elimination of cycles will depend upon the skill that speculators achieve in forecasting supply and consumption responses to prices. Experience with the older markets suggests that as the speculative base is broadened through futures trading the quality of the speculative job will be improved.

Reduction in cyclical variation in production will result in increased efficiency in production and processing. It will be possible to use facilities at a higher percentage of capacity; with cyclical variation, some processing capacity is idle much of the time.

Reduction in cyclical variation will result in increased market size. As noted, consumers do not really need much of the livestock products that we are able to sell them. Merchandising programs to increase sales are more effective as supplies and prices are stable.

Third, futures markets offer money lenders — bankers — security for loans to a much greater extent than has been the case in the past. The producer who sells futures contracts has much greater income security than the one who does not. I think that the strongest influence in getting producers to use futures markets will be the requirements of bankers in financing production.

Fourth, futures markets offer processors stable supplies. It will, indeed, be unfortunate if meat packers buy futures with the intention of taking delivery. More likely and better, they will contract for cash supplies on fixed delivery schedules, and hedge these forward purchases in futures. This appears to be the way that the hog market is developing.

Fifth, futures markets offer distributors an opportunity to develop merchandising programs without the risk of price increases. I should expect this use of futures to be limited because it leaves distributors vulnerable to the risks of price declines.

Sixth, futures markets offer speculators new opportunities for profit. By the same token they offer speculators new opportunities for losses. But this is the kind of world in which speculators live and thrive.

There has been a great deal of effort put into forecasting the supply, demand, and price of livestock and meat. Much useful work has been done, but the results are far from accurate. There is room for improvement and the opportunity for speculative profits will provide the incentive. During the past two years, much new information and analysis of beef cattle prices has come into being. We will see more as speculators increasingly tackle the job.

In this discussion, I have tried to emphasize the role of the speculator and his needs. For altogether too long we have sold futures trading on the basis of risk shifting and treated the speculator as a necessary evil. If these new futures markets simply serve as a means of shifting risks, only a part of their potential will have been achieved. I think that the greater contribution of futures trading is toward more stable prices. And this is the role of the speculator.

Concern with growth. I think that my concern with the future of futures trading is readily apparent. I trust that I have made my enthusiasm for the new developments equally apparent. It is incumbent on all of us who work in this area to promote widespread use by producers, processors, and distributors as well as to assist in the development of a large group of competent speculators.

There are three routes that we can go in the pricing of agricultural products in the increasingly commercial agricultural world; three routes in the search for greater price stability. First, toward governmental price establishment, second, toward vertical integration and dominance by a small number of large firms, and third, toward larger futures markets. I think that in the third direction lies the maximum competitive efficiency and maximum individual opportunity and freedom.

Paper presented at the Livestock and Meats Futures Study Conference-Chicago on November 30, 1966.

[199]

SUMMARY AND PERSPECTIVE

by
The Editor

Unlike a Futures transaction where one man's gain is another man's loss, the ideas expressed in conferences, such as these, redound to the benefit of every participant. The publication of the proceedings makes this knowledge accessible to many who may desire to study our deliberations beyond the confines of these Halls and countless others through eras other than our own. An attempt is made in these closing paragraphs to highlight a few points of agreement on which greater emphasis is pardonable as well as to recapitulate issues where notions diverged sharply among the conferees.

The relatively recent addition of futures contracts applicable to perishable commodities such as meats and livestock was generally regarded with favor by those attending the conferences. This method of buying, selling, and pricing adds another dimension to market services hitherto unavailable.

The existence of a futures market serves to attract increasing amounts of equity capital for financing production, and to expedite market functions. Capital requirements often exceed the financial resources of individual ranchers, feeders, and packers, consequently, greater accessibility to funds is considered a boon to the livestock industry.

Forward pricing makes it possible to plan production more precisely to demand requirements, and it permits the distributors of meat products to direct supplies into market channels with a higher degree of efficiency than prevailed under a unipartite cash market.

The futures market offers greater flexibility to sellers in their choice of buyers, in timing transfers of ownership, and in selecting the markets to which they make deliveries.

Ordinarily, under the cash market system, the ranchers and feeders were required to raise and feed livestock if they wished

[201]

to earn a livelihood. The advent of a futures market makes it possible to cut in and out of production activities, and concentrate partially or solely in buying and selling futures. If price movements and trends are anticipated fairly accurately, profits can be realized by speculating in futures. Playing the role of a speculator is no stranger to livestock producers. The futures market serves to enlarge the stage upon which actors may present this drama of life. Anyone familiar with the industry would find it difficult to disclaim this dynamic attribute of futures trading even though the pot of gold at the end of the rainbow may be capriciously elusive. The risk element in livestock feeding can be substantially reduced, but not completely eliminated by entering into hedging transactions. This process of matching a sale against a purchase, or a purchase against a sale is a form of insurance covering abnormal losses due to wide gyrations in market prices.

The areas of disagreement among those participating in the current series of conferences will be of interest to scholars for years to come if their sense of perception is not greatly improved over their antecedents. Those who espouse the cause for trading in futures have steadfastly maintained that forward pricing serves to stabilize the market by shearing off the peaks and filling the valleys of the sawtooth price lines normally evolved in cash markets.

The adversaries are equally adamant in asserting that futures trading is the chief cause of wide fluctuations in price quotations. They conclude without empirical evidence that traders in the Commodity Exchanges conspire to create price fluctuations. Otherwise, they argue, there would be no profit potentials in contract trading because the institution would self-destruct by actually ironing out prices to the extent there would be no undulations. The protagonists retort, "This is the reasoning of one who has a hole in his wig" because it assumed that the professional traders can individually and independently appraise all dimensions of supply and demand so precisely and simultaneously that each variable factor is brought under their complete control. This is a degree of coordination in collective sagacity no societal institution has ever attained:

GENERAL OBSERVATIONS

"Twixt the optimist and pessimist
The difference is droll:
The optimist sees the doughnut
But the pessimist sees the hole."

During the past century, one commodity after another has burst the bonds of the cash market and edged its way into the pits of Commodity Exchanges. On each occasion the novelty of the transition is still so unique that it causes the sages to ponder whether the intruder is suitable and admissible to the esoteric circle. Differences in point of view on this issue appear to stem from an objective analysis, on the one hand, in which physical attributes of the commodity are subordinated to the legalistic elements of a transfer in ownership. The challenge to this stance emerges from a subjective attitude in which the contender maintains that distinct differences in corporeal features of the commodity ultimately determine whether the commodity under consideration can persevere in contract trading.

From time to time the question of *basis* trading comes to the surface in conclaves such as these, wherein some practitioners declare that they enter into hedging contracts for the sole purpose of realizing profits from the transactions. The *basis* is the difference in the cash price being paid at the local market, and the price quoted for a particular futures contract in a central market. The local price ordinarily is less than the futures quotation due to transportation, holding (storage), interest, and insurance costs. These costs are quite variable; so knowledgeable traders can make commitments when the basis differentials are narrow and divest themselves of the obligation when they widen. In a strict technical sense, the theorists disclaim such profits on the grounds that they are a misnomer. They maintain that whatever profits are realized in such situations should be attributed to handling and service cost differentials reflected in the cash market rather than from variations in the futures price and from transactional negotiations.

Another phenomenon that gives cause for conjecture is the appearance and disappearance of certain futures contracts on the Commodity Exchanges. Why do some futures contracts survive, ad infinitum, while others fail ignominiously? It has been hypothesized that one possible cause for failure is the high correlation in prices persisting between two futures contracts representing closely related products such as flour and wheat; barley and corn; wool tops and greasy wool. Another explanation might be found in locational differences. If there is to be compatibility, the closely related futures should not be offered in the same market unless they provide a sharply delineated service to justify this existence as can be illustrated by the presence of soybean, soybean meal, and soybean oil contracts in the same Commodity Exchange. Can it be concluded from this line of reasoning that the livehog contract is doomed because the pork belly futures contract on the same Exchange is eminently successful? Clearly, this is an intriguing area that should appeal to researchers of the future. Possibly the highest point of contention extracted from the foregoing papers and comments is focused on the function of pricing. One finds among others such statements as:

The primary role of a futures market is one of determining prices for the present, and projecting them into the future.

Although the mechanism for registering prices in future months is provided, — this is not in itself a faculty for accurate projection of prices.

The futures market is the dominant market because it serves as a guide for pricing cash deliveries.

The view that the futures market is the dominant institution is unacceptable.

Futures prices are determined primarily by hedging, hence such "forecasts" as are implied in futures prices are the "forecasts" of hedging firms.

Clearly, much more research effort is urgently needed relative to the function of pricing, particularly in the futures markets. What is the true role of the position (speculative) trader, the broker, the scalper, the odd-lot dealer, the hedger, and the arbitrager (spreader)? How is it possible for hedgers to exert influence, if any, in pricing when in many instances only a small percentage of the transactions are classified as hedges? This question is especially pertinent when hedgers are presumably engaged in merely off-setting a cash transaction with an opposite and equal futures transaction which counter-balances any price judgement he may have given expression to in such transactions.

Is the classical concept of hedging entirely passé?

Finally, it has been suggested that the transitional markets covering the vast area between the cash and futures markets i.e. "Contract to deliver" and "Contract to arrive" agreements have been almost completely neglected by researchers. This could be one aspect of marketing which might be especially rewarding to those who find it possible to muster the necessary resources for investigation.

Appendix A

Terms of a Live Cattle Futures Contract

Par Delivery

A par delivery unit is 40,000 lbs. of Choice Grade Live Steers.

(a) Steers averaging within the weight range of 1050-1150 lbs.; estimated yield requirements to be 61%.

(b) Steers averaging within the weight range of 1151-1250 lbs.; estimated yield requirements to be 62%.

Delivery units with estimated yield under par will be acceptable with allowance of $\frac{1}{4}¢$ per lb. for each $\frac{1}{2}\%$ or less by which the estimated yield is under par.

A par delivery unit must consist of steers averaging within the weight range of 1050-1150 lbs. or steers averaging within the weight range of 1151-1250 lbs., provided that individual steers shall weigh not more than 100 pounds over or under the average weight of the steers in the delivery unit.

Deliveries are usually made at Chicago if such are made, and if sellers desire, they may choose to deliver at either Omaha Nebr. or Kansas City, Mo.

Substitutions and Allowances

Steers weighing from 100 to 200 pounds over or under the average weight of the steers in the delivery unit shall be deliverable at an allowance of $2¢$ per pound. For purposes of computing such allowance, the weight of such steers weighing over or under the average weight of the load shall be considered the same as the average weight per head of the delivered unit. Steers weighing more than 200 pounds over or under the average weight of the load are not acceptable. The judgment of the grader (s) as to the number of such overweight or underweight cattle in the delivery unit shall be final and shall be so certified on the grading certificate.

Delivery units containing not more than 8 head of the top half of USDA Good Grade steers may be substituted at a $2¢$ per pound allowance. For the purpose of computing such allowances, the weight of such Good Grade steers shall be considered the same as the average weight per head of the delivered unit.

Delivery units containing 9 head but not more than 17 head of the top half of USDA Good Grade steers may be substituted at 3¢ per pound allowance. For the purpose of computing such allowances, the weight of such Good Grade steers shall be considered the same as the average weight per head of the delivered unit.

The estimated minimum par yield on Good Grade cattle in the 1000-1150 weight range shall be 58%. The minimum par yield on Good Grade cattle in the 1150-1300 weight range shall be 59%.

USDA Good Grade Steers with an estimated yield under par will be acceptable with an allowance of 1/4¢ per pound for each 1/2% or less by which the estimated yield is under par.

Variations in quantity of a delivery unit not in excess of 5% of 40,000 pounds, shall be permitted at time of delivery.

Futures Call

Futures contracts shall be scheduled for trading and for delivery in such months as may be determined by the Board of Governors.

Commission and Clearance Fee

Commission and clearance fees for non-members of the Exchange on a round-turn transaction are $36.00 per contract.

Termination of Trading

Trading for future delivery in Live Beef Cattle shall terminate on the 20th calendar day of the contract month or the last business day prior thereto.

Deliveries Against Futures Contracts

Deliveries shall be permitted on each Monday, Tuesday, Wednesday and Thursday of the contract month which follow the sixth calendar day of the contract month.

Notice of Intent to Deliver

A seller making delivery must give the Clearing House a written "Notice of Intent to Deliver" in a form prescribed by the Exchange, and such notice must be delivered to the Clearing House not later than 1:00 P.M. (1) one business day prior to actual delivery, and the buyer shall be notified no later than 2:00 P.M. of said day. A Clearing Member shall not be able to liquidate a long position after being notified by the Clearing House that a delivery has been assigned to such an open position. If the seller fails to present deliverable cattle on the date and place specified in the Notice, he shall be penalized ½¢ per pound each day until the requirements are met.

Permissible Change of Contract

All deliveries must conform to governmental regulations in force at the time of delivery. If any Federal Governmental Agency issues an order, ruling, directive or law that conflicts with the requirements of these rules, such order, ruling, directive or law shall be construed to take precedence and become part of these rules and all open and new contracts shall be subject to such Government Orders.

Price Fluctuation on Futures Call

Minimum price fluctuation on the futures call shall be 2½/100¢ per pound. Daily fluctuations are limited to 1¢ (100 points) per pound, upward or downward from the previous day's settling price.

Speculative Position Limits

No person may at any time own, control, or have a proprietary interest in more than a total of 750 cattle contracts long and/or short, with a maximum of 300 in any one month, nor shall any individual, customer, or firm exceed the above limits in any single day's trading.

While restricted to the foregoing position limits, no person during one day, shall trade more than 1,125 beef cattle contracts, with a maximum of 450 in any one month. Bona fide hedging transactions shall not be affected by these limits. *Effective with 1970 contracts, no person may at any time own, control or have a proprietary interest in excess of 300 contracts in each delivery month.*

Trading Hours

Daily from 9:05 A.M. to 12:40 P.M.

Appendix B

Table 1

PRICE RANGES OF LIVE BEEF CATTLE FUTURES CONTRACTS[1]

Season's Price Ranges of Live Beef Cattle Contracts on the Chicago Mercantile Exchange

FEBRUARY CONTRACTS

Year	Open	High	Low	Close
1966	25.50	28.30	24.22	27.65@.55
1967	29.50	29.50	24.67	25.07@.45
1968	28.40	29.45	25.02	27.90@.65

APRIL CONTRACTS

Year	Open	High	Low	Close
1965	24.00	26.50	22.82	26.25@26.00
1966	25.00	29.20	24.20†	27.10@26.75
1967	27.15	29.50	24.85	24.95
1968§	29.30	29.42	24.50	......

JUNE CONTRACTS

Year	Open	High	Low	Close
1965	24.50	28.60	22.95	28.00@28.50
1966	25.00	29.00	24.95	25.60@.15
1967	28.97	29.92	25.40	25.95@.50
1968§	28.30	28.80	24.65	......

JULY CONTRACT

Year	Open	High	Low	Close
1968§	28.22	28.35	25.02†	......

AUGUST CONTRACTS

Year	Open	High	Low	Close
1965	25.00	27.92	23.30	26.75@.27
1966	27.50	29.32	25.00	25.90@26.00
1967	29.90	29.90	25.95	27.40@.07
1968§	25.70	26.95	25.45	......

SEPTEMBER CONTRACT

Year	Open	High	Low	Close
1968	25.50	26.50	25.40	......

OCTOBER CONTRACTS

Year	Open	High	Low	Close
1965	24.75	27.97	23.45	27.97@26.60
1966	28.50	29.47	25.00	25.05@.20
1967	29.70	29.70	26.25	26.50@.25
1968§	25.70	26.95	25.45	......

NOVEMBER CONTRACT

Year	Open	High	Low	Close
1968	25.70	26.35*	26.67†	......

DECEMBER CONTRACTS

Year	Open	High	Low	Close
1965	24.50	27.35	23.85	26.75@.55
1966	29.00	29.77	24.10	24.30@.50
1967	29.50	30.25	25.10	26.20@.35
1968§	25.75	26.70	25.65	......

§ Prices are for life of contract as of March 31, 1967.
* Bid.   † Asked.   ‡ Nominal.

[1] The reader, may bring these statistics up to date by examining the annual report of the Chicago Mercantile Exchange or by writing directly to the Exchange.

FUTURES TRADING IN LIVESTOCK

Figure 1

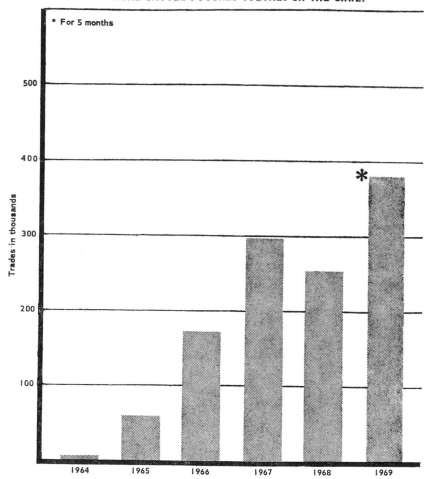

ANNUAL CATTLE FUTURES VOLUMES ON THE C.M.E.

For the entire year 1969, annual cattle futures reached the volume of 1,013,671 trades.

Table 2

CATTLE AND CALVES ON FEED

(In Thousand Head)

Year	No. of States	Jan. 1	Apr. 1	July 1	Oct. 1
1959	26	6,601	Not Available	Not Available	5,012
1960	26	7,212	6,716	5,690	5,161
1961	26	7,686	7,168	5,890	5,684
1962	28	8,194	7,525	6,280	6,322
1963	28	9,354	8,478	7,210	7,175
1964	32	9,704	9,006	7,245	7,222
1965	32	9,844	8,985	7,928	7,738
1966	32	10,436	10,226	8,858	8,424
1967	32	11,125	10,483	8,730	8,591
1968	32	11,297	10,671	....	....

CATTLE AND CALVES ON FARMS, JANUARY 1, U. S.*

NUMBER, BY CLASSES

(In Thousand Head)

Year	Cows 2 Yrs. and Older	Heifers 1-2 Yrs. Old	Calves	Steers 1 Yr. and Older	Bulls 1 Yr. and Older	Total
1955	25,659	6,514	18,804	8,444	1,829	61,250
1956	25,371	6,206	18,869	9,483	1,762	61,691
1957	24,534	5,926	18,405	8,991	1,713	59,569
1958	24,165	5,903	18,275	9,252	1,619	59,214
1959	25,112	6,557	19,407	9,931	1,607	62,614
1960	26,344	7,036	20,425	10,574	1,676	66,055
1961	27,327	7,115	20,814	10,997	1,714	67,967
1962	28,691	7,446	22,300	11,103	1,715	71,255
1963	30,589	8,108	23,747	12,251	1,771	76,466
1964	32,794	8,612	25,243	12,669	1,851	81,169
1965	34,238	8,989	26,181	12,134	1,908	83,450
1966	34,433	8,925	26,879	12,749	1,878	84,864
1967	34,685	9,121	27,294	12,752	1,870	85,722
1968**	35,300	9,312	27,507	12,568	1,895	86,582

* Excludes Dairy Cattle   ** Preliminary.

Table 3

COMMERCIAL CATTLE SLAUGHTER*
TOTAL LIVE WEIGHT, 48 STATES
(In Million Pounds)

	Jan.	Feb.	Mar.	April	May	June	July	Aug.	Sep.	Oct.	Nov.	Dec.	Total
1955	1,975	1,701	1,971	1,840	1,954	2,077	1,903	2,245	2,214	2,157	2,115	2,049	24,201
1956	2,223	1,960	2,024	2,007	2,129	2,112	2,164	2,202	2,042	2,445	2,258	2,117	25,683
1957	2,414	1,950	1,976	1,951	2,160	1,958	2,210	2,172	2,090	2,322	1,975	1,948	25,126
1958	2,193	1,740	1,800	1,836	1,902	1,926	2,033	1,907	2,033	2,170	1,755	1,944	23,242
1959	1,987	1,673	1,806	1,926	1,872	1,943	2,044	1,891	2,058	2,090	1,922	2,043	23,256
1960	2,105	1,914	2,110	1,872	2,103	2,189	2,044	2,289	2,292	2,236	2,126	2,051	25,331
1961	2,181	1,906	2,167	1,985	2,282	2,305	2,119	2,328	2,198	2,341	2,187	2,061	26,060
1962	2,339	1,940	2,150	1,990	2,289	2,215	2,239	2,365	2,106	2,402	2,163	2,022	26,220
1963	2,364	2,042	2,212	2,248	2,416	2,262	2,371	2,410	2,327	2,647	2,281	2,313	27,891
1964	2,622	2,232	2,441	2,614	2,602	2,742	2,674	2,590	2,692	2,867	2,587	2,773	31,440
1965	2,695	2,389	2,747	2,493	2,503	2,680	2,677	2,769	2,869	2,850	2,812	2,828	32,316
1966†	2,929	2,593	2,826	2,634	2,793	2,953	2,712	3,023	2,969	2,896	2,886	2,860	34,085
1967†	3,005	2,669	2,938	2,739	3,020	2,990	2,740	2,994	2,850	3,001	2,828	2,771	34,545

* Figures through 1965 includes slaughter under federal inspection and other commercial slaughter; excludes farm slaughter.
† Effective January 1966, figures include custom slaughtering in plants for farmers. This inclusion is expected to increase total slaughter by 1 to 2%.

Table 4

HOG FUTURES SEASON HIGHS & LOWS

Crop High & Low Prices on the Chicago Mercantile Exchange

JANUARY DELIVERY

Year		Open	High	Low	Close
1968	......	20.00	20.00	18.65	19.25@.45

FEBRUARY DELIVERY

Year		Open	High	Low	Close
1967	......	18.50	23.00	18.25	20.00@.40*
1968	......	19.50	21.30	18.60	20.80@.85

MARCH DELIVERY

Year		Open	High	Low	Close
1968	......	19.00	19.60	18.50	19.50@.30

APRIL DELIVERY

Year		Open	High	Low	Close
1967	......	19.00	22.50	18.95	19.00@.25
1968§	....	19.50	19.75	18.60	......

MAY DELIVERY

Year		Open	High	Low	Close
1968§	....	19.50	20.00	19.10	......

JUNE DELIVERY

Year		Open	High	Low	Close
1967	......	21.50	25.60	20.95	23.25
1968§	....	20.00	20.85	19.50	......

* Bid.   † Asked.   ‡ Nominal.
§ Through March 15.

JULY DELIVERY

Year		Open	High	Low	Close
1966	......	26.50	26.50	23.40	25.20@24.50
1967	......	23.00	25.45	22.00	23.50@.40
1968§	....	20.00	21.25	19.45†	......

AUGUST DELIVERY

Year		Open	High	Low	Close
1966	......	24.55	27.20	22.50	27.15@.00
1967	......	23.00	25.50	21.50	21.50@.75*
1968§	....	20.00	20.45	19.50	......

SEPTEMBER DELIVERY

Year		Open	High	Low	Close
1966	......	22.50	26.40	20.85†	24.20@.00
1967	......	22.00	24.00	18.90	19.25
1968§	....	19.75	19.75	19.00	......

OCTOBER DELIVERY

Year		Open	High	Low	Close
1966	......	22.05	24.30	19.75	21.00
1967	......	21.50	22.75	18.75	18.75@19.00*

NOVEMBER DELIVERY

Year		Open	High	Low	Close
1966	......	20.25	23.80	19.00	23.00@22.50
1967	......	21.00	22.75	18.40	18.75@.50

DECEMBER DELIVERY

Year		Open	High	Low	Close
1966	......	20.00	22.75	18.90	22.00@22.50
1967	......	21.25	23.00	18.50	18.67@.80*

FUTURES TRADING IN LIVESTOCK

Figure 2

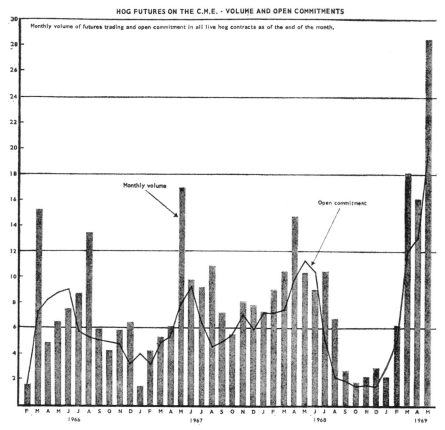

HOG FUTURES ON THE C.M.E. - VOLUME AND OPEN COMMITMENTS

Total number of contracts traded in 1969 was **63,869.**
As of December 31, 1969, open commitments in live hogs were reported to be **3,065.**

Table 5

U. S. SOWS FARROWING

NUMBER OF SOWS FARROWED IN THE U.S. BY QUARTERS

(In Thousand Head)

	Dec.-Feb.	Mar.-May	June-Aug.	Sep.-Nov.
1959	3,053	4,943	3,346	2,782
1960	2,507	4,275	3,035	2,804
1961	2,521	4,497	3,081	2,837
1962	2,580	4,416	3,141	2,957
1963	2,593	4,506	3,125	2,862
1964	2,366	4,230	2,903	2,622
1965	2,178	3,712	2,548	2,458
1966	2,220	3,981	3,009	2,805
1967	2,450	4,120	2,974	2,925
1968	2,549	4,131	3,162	2,994
1969	(Dec-May Ind. 6,981)		....	....

Table 6

U. S. SPRING & FALL PIG CROPS

NUMBER OF PIGS SAVED AND THE NUMBER SAVED PER LITTER

SPRING CROP —	Pigs Saved (In Thou.)	Sows Farrowing (In Thou.)	Pigs Saved Per Litter
1959	56,620	7,996	7.08
1960	47,288	6,782	6.96
1961	50,366	7,018	7.18
1962	49,535	6,996	7.08
1963	50,749	7,099	7.15
1964	47,682	6,596	7.23
1965	42,525	5,890	7.22
1966	45,422	6,201	7.32
1967	48,205	6,570	7.34
*1968	49,226	6,680	7.37
**1969	51,700	6,981	7.40
FALL CROP —			
1958	42,179	5,887	7.17
1959	42,775	6,128	6.98
1960	40,998	5,839	7.02
1961	42,347	5,918	7.16
1962	44,073	6,098	7.23
1963	43,307	5,987	7.23
1964	39,862	5,525	7.21
1965	36,415	5,006	7.27
1966	42,141	5,811	7.25
1967	43,540	5,899	7.38
*1968	45,270	6,156	7.35

*Preliminary   **Indications

Table 7

HOG SLAUGHTER

NUMBER SLAUGHTER MONTHLY UNDER FEDERAL INSPECTION IN U.S.

(In Thousand Head)

	Jan.	Feb.	Mar.	April	May	June	July	Aug.	Sep.	Oct.	Nov.	Dec.	Total
1955	5,519	4,638	5,491	4,472	4,164	3,713	3,428	4,475	5,144	6,144	6,857	7,324	61,370
1956	6,705	5,922	6,327	5,252	4,875	4,326	4,199	4,559	4,979	6,347	6,559	5,698	65,748
1957	5,655	4,985	5,380	5,000	4,884	3,994	4,185	4,418	5,060	6,094	5,505	5,523	60,682
1958	5,531	4,453	4,818	4,963	4,444	4,209	4,326	4,515	5,219	5,911	5,258	5,814	59,462
1959	5,885	5,686	5,733	5,652	4,970	4,902	5,184	4,977	5,767	6,646	6,337	6,968	68,707
1960	6,516	5,841	6,116	5,571	5,483	5,086	4,304	5,203	5,165	5,407	5,707	5,753	66,153
1961	5,744	5,078	6,110	5,049	5,597	5,093	4,320	5,114	5,240	6,223	6,327	5,738	65,632
1962	6,098	5,312	6,225	5,672	5,800	5,041	4,699	5,214	4,737	6,643	6,376	5,954	67,770
1963	6,333	5,665	6,559	6,343	5,910	4,880	4,995	5,174	5,868	6,775	6,379	6,695	71,557
1964	6,956	5,898	6,420	6,481	5,476	5,038	4,928	4,841	5,630	6,804	6,546	6,648	71,667
1965	6,047	5,301	6,534	5,802	4,719	4,717	4,429	4,750	5,475	5,421	5,503	5,010	63,708
1966	4,719	4,650	5,806	5,303	4,913	4,673	4,228	5,088	5,888	6,047	6,200	6,215	63,729
1967	6,281	5,661	6,728	5,867	5,310	5,178	4,743	5,808	6,115	6,684	6,431	6,100	70,890
1968	6,496	5,679	6,238	6,483	6,407	5,125	5,454	5,942	6,348	7,404	6,571	......	......

Appendix C

Some Classroom Exercises in the Use of Future Contracts in Marketing Cattle

by
M. Brice Kirtley
University of Illinois

The information we have here is the material that has been used for the class in livestock marketing. It's very elementary, considering the presentation you have had this morning. I think it fits, though. First, it does indicate to you, in the trade, some of the approaches that we are trying to make with students to understand the operations of futures markets for live animals. Secondly, it represents an approach that we have used with students and other groups, fairly satisfactorily, to explain what actually is involved. Perhaps some of you may be able to use it or some adaption of the materials for discussing it with people who are interested in the activities of a futures market.

I think that you should realize, of course, that this is only one portion of the materials that we do use in discussing futures trading with the students. It is supplemented by readings, lectures, and actual visits to the Mercantile Exchange when the class makes their market tour.

Students are particularly interested in futures trading in the livestock marketing course, inasmuch as this is a new development. They have some of the same problems that many farmers have in thinking of the futures market. Firstly, is viewing it as a physical means of disposing of livestock, i.e., thinking in terms of particular cattle or in terms of a marketing channel. Secondly, viewing it as a mysterious paper transaction that really doesn't mean much relating to the actual level of cash prices. I think that some of the problems outlined here help to let students understand the relationships involved.

In understanding the operation of futures market, the use of numerical samples can be quite helpful. My colleague, Professor Broadbent, has developed the following set of problems, and he was to have discussed them with you today. We have found these illustrations to be quite helpful in explaining the operation of future markets to students and other groups of persons. For most of you, these illustrations will be very elementary, but they indicate an approach to explaining futures operations.

A Hedging Contract in Cattle Futures (Favorable)

Example #1: Fixing A Sales Price Against A Price Decline.

	Price Per Cwt	Return Per Animal	
		Cash Market	Futures Market
A Livestock Feeder:		(At Feedlot)	(At Chicago)
1. On January 1 *Buys* 600 lb. feeders @	$22.00	$132.00	
Puts on 400 lb. of gain @ cost of	$25.00	$100.00	
Selling weight, 1,000 lb. choice total cost		$232.00	
(Break-even selling price 1,000 lb.)	$23.20		
2. On January 1, *Sells* June futures for 1,000 lb. choice steers @	$25.00		$250.00
3. On June 1, *Sells* 1,000 lb. fat steers for cash @	$22.00	$220.00	
4. On June 1, *Buys* back June futures for 1,000 lb. steers @	$22.00		$220.00
Loss or gain per head		—$ 12.00	+$ 30.00
Loss or gain per contract of 25,000 lb. of live choice steers*		—$300.00	+$750.00

*Less cost of commission and interest on margin capital.
($25.00 per round-turn contract = $1.00 per head commission.)

1. Net profit from hedging = $18.00 per head less $1.40 for commission charges and interest on margin capital, or $16.00 per head.

2. Net profit per contract through hedging = $16.60 × 25 head, or $415.00.

A Hedging Contract in Cattle Futures (Unfavorable)

Example #2: Fixing a Sales Price on a Rising Market.

	Price Per Cwt	Return Per Animal	
		Cash Market	Futures Market
		(At Feedlot)	(At Chicago)
A Livestock Feeder:			
1. On January 1, Buys 600 lb. feeders @	$22.00	$132.00	
400 lb. of gain @ cost of	$25.00	$100.00	
Selling weight, 1,000 lb. total cost		$232.00	
(Break-even selling price, 1,000 lb.)	$23.20		
2. On January 1, *Sells* June futures for 1,000 lb. steers @	$25.00		$250.00
3. On June 1, *Sells* 1,000 lb. fat steers for cash @	$28.00	$280.00	
4. On June 1, *Buys* back June futures for 1,000 lb. steers @	$28.00		$280.00
Loss or gain per head		+$ 48.00	—$ 30.00
Loss or gain per contract of 25,000 lb. of live choice steers*		+$1,200.00	—$750.00

*Less cost of commission and interest on margin capital.

1. Net profit if operator had not hedged = $48.00 per head. (25 head lot)

2. Net profit after hedging = $16.00 ($18.00 less $1.40 per head for commission and interest on margin capital).

3. Amount of profit missed as result of hedging = $31.40 per head.

Livestock Marketing — Cattle Futures

Hypothetical Example #3 of Speculator's Transactions
With a Live Cattle Futures Contract (Buy) (Long)

(One contract = 25,000 pounds of live cattle — $25 round-turn)
(Every change of $1.00 per cwt = $250 per contract)

Day	Activity	Price Per cwt.	Margin	Position[1] value balance	Value of Contract
1	Buys 1 June contract @	$25.00	$300	$300.00	$6,250.00
2	(a) Market advances	$26.00	$300	$550.00	$6,500.00
	(b) Collects $250.00 surplus margin.		$300	$300.00	$6,500.00
3	(a) Market declines	$25.50	$200	$175.00	$6,375.00
	(b) Pays broker $125.00		$300	$300.00	$6,375.00
4	(a) Market Declines	$25.00	$200	$175.00	$6,250.00
	(b) Pays broker $125.00 to maintain margin.		$300	$300.00	$6,250.00
5	(a) Market declines	$24.75	$200	$237.50	$6,187.50
6	(a) Market declines	$24.50	$200	$175.00	$6,125.00
	(b) Pay broker $125.00		$300	$300.00	$6,125.00
7	(a) Market declines	$24.00	$200	$165.00	$6,000.00
	(b) Pays broker $125.00 to to maintain margin		$300	$300.00	$6,000.00
8	(a) Sells out contract and clears out with $............ margin less $............ commission.	$24.00	....	$300.00	$6,000.00

Investment in selling one contract			Day	Receipts		P or L	
Day							
1	Original margin	$300	2	Collects	$250	Invested	$800
3	Added margin	$125	8	Clears out	$300	Received	$550
4	Added margin	$125		Received	$550	Loss	$250
6	Added margin	$125				Interest	$ 18
7	Added margin	$125				Broker fee	$ 25
		$800				Total Loss	$295

Interest: 6% × 6 mo. × 600 + $18.00

[1] A $300 margin is required, but a minimum maintenance margin balance of $200
is required per contract. A purchase makes money if the price goes up, and a
sale loses money if the price goes up. The trader must realize that the losses
and gains are real — Not Just Paper Profits.

APPENDIX C

Hypothetical Example #4 of Speculator's Transactions With a Live Cattle Futures Contract (Sell) (Short)

(One contract = 25,000 pounds of live cattle — $25 round-turn)
(Every change of $1.00 per cwt. = $250 per contract)

Day	Activity	Price	Margin	Position value balance	Value of Contract
1	Sells 1 June Contract @	$25.00	....	....	....
2	(a) Market advances	$26.00	....	....	....
	(b) Puts up $............. more margin		....	....	....
3	(a) Market declines	$25.50	....	....	....
4	(a) Market declines	$25.00	....	....	....
5	(a) Market declines	$24.75	....	....	....
6	(a) Market declines	$24.50	....	....	....
	(6) Collects $.............		....	....	....
7	(a) Market declines	$24.00	....	....	....
8	(a) Buys back contract @	$24.00	....	....	....
	Clears out at				
	Margin (Less				
	Commission)				

Investment in Buying One Contract

Day		Receipts Day		P or L		Interest
1	Original margin $.............	6	$.............	Investment $.............		@6%×6
2	Added margin	8	....	Gross gain		mo. ×
	$.............		$.............	Less Commiss.		500 =
				Gross Return		$.............
				Less interest		
				Net profit		

NOTE: The trader is simply trading in contract. The margin requires a trader to deposit a marginal sum of money to back up his Commitment or be cleared out. To show how the value difference is determined, we illustrate with a contract that is the actual cash value of one contract on each of the days listed. Remember, the trader only puts up a margin to maintain his position.

A "bearish" speculator *sells* because he anticipates that the price will decline, and he hopes to gain from a falling market. He hopes to cover at a lower price than that at which he sold. He profits or absorbs the loss from such transaction.

The first illustration is a real success story. The cattle feeder purchases cattle for the feedlot at $22 per hundred. He knows it will cost him a hundred dollars to add an additional 400 pounds gain. This means he will have to have a $23.20 break-even price. By selling a futures contract, he gets not $23.20, but $25.00. When the actual time of sale has arrived, the cash market has declined to $22.00. Therefore, by selling his cattle in advance for $25.00 per hundred weight when he put them in the feed lot, he nets $415 more on each contract then would have been possible had he fed the cattle without a forward sale. There are several points which need to be emphasized in connection with this problem. First, a cattle feeder needs to be well informed of his costs of feeding, so that he knows what figure will give him a satisfactory return. In the example used, $25.00 per hundred was a sufficient amount to cover all costs. This, a feeder needs to know from his own records, and not from ordinary averages. Second is that the feeder actually establishes a selling price at the time that the cattle were put into the feed lot. A futures market adds a dimension of flexibility in time by pricing his product weeks or months before actual delivery. The feeder might have waited until he had the cattle on feed for a period of time before actually establishing a price. Any time from prior to the time of being placed into the feed lot to actual delivery, cattle can be priced through the futures market. Moreover, should the trend of the market indicate that a mistake had been made in making a forward sale, the feeder might be able to execute an off-setting transaction thus feeding the cattle unhedged putting him in a position to take advantage of a rising cash market. These are areas in which the cattle feeder has an opportunity to make decisions which may be profitable to him. Previous speakers have made reference to quality or locational differentials. For simplicity, these have not been included in this problem, but may need to be considered in individual cases.

Turning to problem #2, this is the same illustration as the previous problem, but in this case, the cash market advanced to $28 rather than declining to $22.00. Again, the feeder required a $23.20 break-even price. At the time he placed his cattle in the feed lot, he sold ahead for $25.00. This then removed most price risk for his feeding operation. It assured him of a return above his break-even price. Yet, because his price was set in advance, he failed to benefit from the additional $3.00 price rise from $25.00 up to $28.00. Had he speculated by feeding the cattle unhedged, he would have gained this amount. This simply points up a disadvantage of forward selling or hedging. You cannot have the best of two worlds. If you are going to remove the risk of a downward price movement, you also have to forego the gains of an upward price trend.

Problem #3 provides an example of the mechanics of a futures operation in live cattle. This illustration indicates the influences of changes in market price on amounts of margin. The last column, value of contract, is listed simply to emphasize that if carried to maturity these contracts could represent substantial sums of money. Usually when this exercise is used for students, they are asked to work through the problem and fill in the blanks. For simplicity, this exercise is completed, but you might be interested in following through the arithmetic of the various steps. You will also note that a 'bullish" speculator buys because he anticipates a price increase and hopes to gain from a rising market. He hopes to sell out for a higher price than that at which he bought.

Problem #4 is simply a reverse of the Problem III. This provides you with an opportunity to go through the step-by-step calculations as was done on Problem III.

In summary, we would hope these problems have served to make some important points about live cattle futures. Live cattle futures provide another tool which the cattle feeder may use in his business operations. To most effectively use this tool, he needs to understand how it operates, and he needs to know his costs. With this information, a futures market provides the feeder an opportunity to forward price his cattle, and very materially reduce price risk involved in his feeding operation.

Paper presented at the Livestock and Meats Futures Study Conference-Chicago on November 30, 1966.

Appendix D

HEDGING WITH LIVE BEEF FUTURES*

1.   On November 30th, 1964, the Chicago Mercantile Exchange opened contract trading in live cattle. This has made it possible for cattle men to hedge their feeding operations.

2.   Cattle feeding is a business fraught with risks. There are many factors which affect prices and profits.

3.   A major cattle feeding risk is that of drastic price changes. Big changes in price are fine—if prices go up. But slumping prices can wipe out profits and may even spell financial ruin.

4.   Cattle feeders can reduce the risks of price declines by hedging in the futures market. Hedging is defined as insuring oneself against adverse circumstances. In this case, hedging is protecting oneself against unfavorable price changes.

* *Based on a series of slides presented by J. Marvin Skadberg, extension economist, and George Brandsberg, assistant extension editor of Iowa State University.*

5. Hedging is a management tool. It can be used to lock in profits, if properly executed.

6. Hedging involves selling and buying futures contracts. Futures contracts are standardized agreements pertaining to the future delivery of a commodity.

7. Commodity futures markets provide a trade center for many buyers and sellers of contracts. It makes it possible to buy or sell contracts at specific prices currently prevailing in the market if a person chooses to enter into such transactions.

8. The main parties involved in a futures contract transaction may be the hedger, the speculator and their brokers.

9. A feeder becomes a hedger when he sells a futures contract, thus establishing a sale price for his cattle. The cash price ultimately received when cattle are delivered may vary appreciably from the futures market commitment. The hedger sells through a broker.

[225]

10. Actual trading of futures contracts is done by brokers who are members of commodity exchanges. Brokers serve as representatives of hedgers and speculators. Brokers, as members of an exchange, must adhere to rules of that exchange.

11. Speculators buy and sell futures contracts. They make two important contributions to a futures market. One, they provide a substantial part of the volume of trade. Volume of trading is important for a successful futures market.

12. Second, speculators assume the financial risk which hedgers wish to avoid, and they do this in hopes of making a profit.

13. In thinking about futures trading and futures contracts, remember there are three major parties to the contract:
   • Hedgers, who seek to reduce risks
   • Speculators, who assume risks in hopes of making a profit, and
   • Brokers, who represent hedgers and speculators

14. As stated previously, the futures contract is a standardized agreement relating to the future delivery of a commodity. In addition to specifying price, the contract specifies the product, the quantity involved, where it shall be delivered, the month of delivery, and the costs involved.

15.   The Chicago Mercantile Exchange futures contract calls for U.S. Choice steers weighing between 1,050 pounds and 1,150 pounds with a dressing yield of 61 percent. There are other contracts on other Exchanges which specify steers of slightly different weights and yields.

16.   The CME contract calls for 40,000 pounds of live steers. About 37 head of cattle weigh enough to fill the contract.

17.   The contracts also list what substitutions may be made. For example, some steers which grade U.S. Good may be used to replace animals of Choice grade, but the hedger must pay a penalty for substitution.

18.   If delivery is made on the contract, it is usually made at Chicago. However, the contract allows for deliveries at Omaha, and Kansas City, Mo. but with a specified price discount.

19.   Contract costs are also spelled out. Since trading is done on a margin basis, a margin deposit is required of all traders. They also must pay brokerage fees. All delivery expenses are paid by the seller.

20. Futures contracts are different from other contracts in that they can be fulfilled in two ways.

21. First, by delivering the cattle according to the contract.

22. Second, by making an offsetting futures trade. That is, the hedger who sold a contract for delivery, say, in October, can "offset" the obligation to make delivery simply by buying an October futures contract. In a sense, he buys back his contract.

23. The hedger initiates the offsetting purchase simply by ordering his broker to buy a contract similar to the one sold at the outset of his hedging operation . . .

24. At the commodity futures exchange, the hedger's broker deals with a broker representing a speculator . . .

25. Simultaneously, a speculator may also want to clear himself of the market. He does this by selling a contract similar to the one he bought through his broker.

26. Once the broker representing the hedger buys an offsetting contract, the hedger is clear of the futures market.

27. Thus, the hedger or the cattle feeder is free to sell his cattle on the open market.

28. When can the cattle feeder buy back a contract? Any time up to the expiration date of the contract which is usually on the 20th of the contract month. If he doesn't buy back a contract, he must deliver, usually after the 20th day of the contract month and before the last business day of the month.

[229]

29. Should one hedge with live beef futures? A realistic decision to hedge must be based on a thorough look at one's situation.

30. This means that one must study his situation. Examine production costs, market trends, marketing expenses, production trends and how they affect his own cattle feeding operation. The next series of illustrations will reveal seven steps to be applied in determining whether one should hedge or not.

31. The first step is to establish a localized futures price. This involves subtracting several cost factors from the Chicago futures price to give one a "localized" price.

32. To localize the Chicago futures price, one must calculate costs of transportation, shrinkage, marketing, brokerage, margin deposit, and an allowance for a quality adjustment.

33. Begin the calculation by estimating the difference in transportation costs from one's farm to the local market. Compare the costs of shipping from the farm to the central market in Chicago. Assume it normally costs 30 cents a hundred to ship to the local market, and 50 cents a hundred to ship to Chicago. The difference—20 cents per hundredweight—is the transportation cost one should subtract from the live beef futures price to bring it down to the local level.

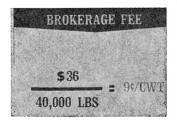

34. It is desirable to allow for additional shrinkage resulting from shipping one's cattle to the more distant market. Suppose animals usually shrink three percent on their way to the local market, but they shrink four percent in transit to Chicago. The cost of the additional one percent of shrink should be taken into account so it, too, can be deducted from the Chicago futures price.

35. Brokerage fees are another expense of hedging, so one should deduct them from the Chicago futures quotation when localizing it. In the conventional live beef futures contract, the broker's fee amounts to $36 per 40,000 pound contract. Therefore, the brokerage fee amounts to 9 cents per hundredweight.

[231]

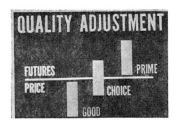

36. Futures contracts are traded on a margin basis, therefore, a margin deposit is required for each contract bought or sold. Basic margin requirements are set by the exchange, but deposit requirements of individual brokers may vary. One major broker requires an initial deposit of $450 for each 40,000-pound contract. Adverse price changes may make it necessary to deposit additional funds.

37. Since the deposit money draws no interest, it must be called a cost. Eight cents per hundredweight is a satisfactory estimate of the margin deposit costs. The exact cost will vary, depending upon how long one has margin money on deposit.

38. Still another consideration in localizing the Chicago futures price is making allowance for some additional marketing costs. One should allow about 35 cents per hundredweight to cover commission fees, feed, yardage and other expenses normally encountered on the terminal market, but only if one should deliver on the contract.

39. The animals one finishes for market will probably vary in quality from the cattle specified by the futures contract. If low-Choice steers are normally delivered, one should deduct a dollar to a dollar and a half per hundredweight from the future price. When hedging U.S. Good slaughter cattle one may need to deduct as much as three or four dollars per hundredweight. This is rather difficult, but an important item to consider in arriving at an estimated local price.

[232]

40. The example in the illustration lists hedging costs—that is, costs of transportation, shrinkage, brokerage fees, interest on margin deposit, market charges and quality adjustment. These add up to $1.75 per hundredweight. Each individual producer's costs may differ from this calculation.

41. The second major step to determine if one shoulld hedge is to estimate when a particular lot of cattle will be ready for market. Once this is done, it will be possible to select the futures contract month and the price to use as a basis for one's calculations.

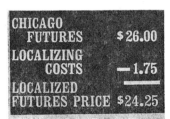

42. The third step involves subtracting the localized costs from the futures price. This will give one an estimated localized futures price. Assume that the quoted futures price is $26. Then subtract the cost of $1.75. The result is a localized futures price of $24.25 as shown in the illustration herewith.

43. The fourth step is to estimate feeder and feeding costs. This gives one an estimate of the cost of putting finished beef on the market. Without these estimates it is impossible to assess the outcome of a hedging operation.

[233]

44.   The fifth major step in analyzing whether one should hedge consists of subtracting ones feeding costs from the localized futures price to estimate how profitable a hedge will be. In the case illustrated here, the cost of feeding is $24 per hundredweight. Hedging in this instance would lock in a return of only 25 cents per hundred. This is an extremely small return to lock in!

45.   Before completing step six it is necessary to carefully study market outlook information. This gives one a basis for estimating prices one may receive for cattle without hedging. Specialists at agricultural colleges prepare such information periodically. Outlook information is also available in farm publications and from private organizations.

46.   The sixth step, then, is to determine the returns without hedging. One subtracts production costs from prices indicated by outlook forecasts. This provides one with an estimate of returns without making a hedge.

47.   The seventh and final step involves comparing estimated returns with and without a hedge. This gives one a basis to decide whether hedging will be advantageous. It is important to remember that hedging with futures is possible because the futures and the cash market tend to come together as a futures contract approaches the maturity date.

[234]

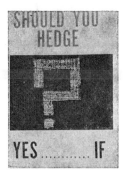

48. Should one hedge? Each feeder has to determine for himself what is a satisfactory return. There are a number of situations in which hedging is desirable.

49. If live cattle prices are expected to decline drastically, one should seriously consider hedging for price protection.

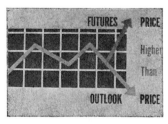

50. If the futures contract price is higher than indicated by outlook forecasts, it might be wise to hedge.

51. When the price outlook situation is uncertain and one cannot afford a loss, hedging, properly used, will provide one protection against adverse price changes.

52.   Let us examine a typical hedging operation such as a feeder might pursue—Suppose one has 100 head of calves in his possession in November.

53.   Assume that the plan is to feed these calves so they'll be ready for market as Choice grade cattle in October of next year.

54.   From past experience and accurate records one knows that the cost of purchasing the calves and feeding them to 1,100 pounds will be about $24 per hundredweight.

55.   Checking on the current Chicago live beef futures price for October of next year, one learns that contracts are being traded at $28 per hundredweight.

56. It has already been determined that the costs for "localizing" the Chicago futures price will approximate $1.75 per hundredweight.

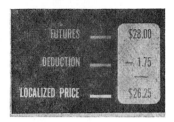

57. Consequently, the localized futures price—which one could expect for cattle in October of next year—will be about $26.25 per hundredweight, using a hedge.

58. By subtracting feeding costs from the localized futures price, one finds that he can expect a profit of $2.25 per hundredweight. Unless there are strong indications that live cattle prices will continue to rise substantially, one will probably decide to hedge.

59. Now let's see what will happen if one hedges and live cattle prices decline.

60. Assume that Choice steer prices on the cash market sink to an average of $24.25 per hundredweight locally after the hedge is made. Considering that production costs will total $24 per hundred. This would leave one with only 25 cents profit per hundred from his feeding operation.

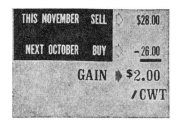

61. But since the prospective seller hedged by selling October futures at $28, and since October futures prices declined at the same time cash prices declined, then he is in a position to buy back October futures at $26. This gives the seller a return of $2 per hundred on his futures transaction.

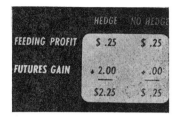

62. By combining a narrow profit from feeding and a gain made in futures trading, one's return with a hedge is $2.25 per hundredweight. This compares with only 25 cents profit per hundredweight with no hedge.

63. Let's back up a moment, and see how one would do if live cattle prices had moved higher during the time one had hedged.

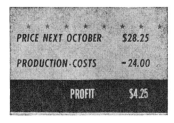

64. By the time the futures contract reaches maturity, Choice steers are selling for an average of $28.25 per hundredweight on the local cash market. This means that one makes $4.25 per hundred profit on one's feeding operation.

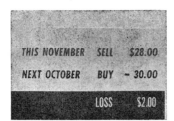

65. While live cattle prices were rising, futures prices were also going up. By October of next year, October futures were being traded at $30 per hundred. one normally buys back futures contracts to clear oneself of the market. In this situation, buying back the futures contract causes the producer to lose two dollars per hundred on his futures transaction.

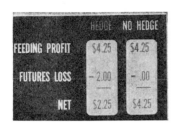

66. The feeding profit, minus the futures loss, gives one a return of $2.25 per hundredweight. This is the same profit that was "locked in" when live cattle prices slipped. But, in this case, a no-hedge position would have given one a return of $4.25 per hundredweight.

67. This example shows that when live beef prices rise, no benefit is realized by hedging. In fact, hedging when cattle prices are rising puts a limit on possible profits. The crux of the matter is to know when prices are going to rise.

68. Two examples of perfect hedges have been illustrated. A perfect hedge occurs when the futures price and the cash price at sale time are identical. In most cases, a hedger will not have a perfect hedge, but often it will be very close.

69.　Several possible situations may produce an imperfect hedge. One case would be where the futures price is above the cash price at sale time. If the difference is large, the hedger will find it more profitable to deliver the cattle rather than repurchase a futures contract.

70.　Another kind of imperfect hedge exists when the futures price is below the cash price. In this instance it is better to repurchase his futures contracts since the hedger will make an additional profit.

71.　Other imperfect hedges would result from inaccurate estimates of the quality of the animals involved, or when price relationships between grades change substantially after the hedge is made.

72.　A review of the main points in hedging with live beef futures at this point may be edifying.

73. Hedging involves trading in the futures market. Futures contracts are bought and sold through brokers.

74. Futures contracts specify not only price but also the product, the quantity, the delivery point, the month of the contract and the costs of trading.

75. It is important that all hedging expenses be calculated. With this information, a hedger is able to determine the possible outcome of a hedge.

76. It is also important that the potential hedger study his own situation. What is good for his neighbor may not be good for him.

77. *Remember,* hedging is a management tool which can be used to lock in profits. But it must be used properly to be to one's advantage.

[241]

NAME INDEX

[243]

NAME INDEX

[244]

SUBJECT INDEX

SUBJECT INDEX